INTEGRATED ELECTRONIC SECURITY
A Layered Approach

A Consultant's Guide to
Electronic Security Systems
Martin Grigg

Integrated Electronic Security – A Layered Approach

Edited by Meridian Media
Published by tectec-press

First edition 2013

ISBN 978-0-9927250-0-6

The information contained within this publication has been gained from reputable sources. However, the author or tectec-press cannot guarantee that it is correct, complete or error-free. This book has been published for guidance only and does not necessarily constitute sound engineering advice for any particular situation.

Martin Grigg is an independent consultant and does not endorse any product or company in this publication, either named or implied.

tectec-press

INTEGRATED ELECTRONIC SECURITY
A Layered Approach

Martin Grigg

Thank you to all of those that have helped with
the production of this book.

Aarron, Debs, Pam, Jeremy,
David, Hasan and Andy.

Preface

I have been working in the electronic security industry for more than 25 years, and from the day that I started as an intruder alarm service engineer – when I was working on domestic alarms in rural Sussex – to just the other day, I have heard claims from 'so-called' industry experts that simply are not correct. People tell me that their product can see things around corners, or is the 'best' product in the industry at video compression. I recall as a CCTV engineer asking the company for whom I worked for a replacement 16mm lens and being told, in all seriousness, that they didn't have a 16mm one and would two 8mm ones do instead! More recently, a very large organisation that is reputedly expert in defence systems with a global presence was brought to my attention when their customer had suspicions that the security scheme being presented wasn't coming together quite as expected. This company who were obviously used to designing high-security perimeter systems – or you would have thought – was having real trouble with today's IP technology.

Time and time again I come across people that have a little knowledge and make false claims or I find people designing systems when they are not qualified or experienced enough to do the job properly. A little knowledge really is a dangerous thing. Because of this, I got into the habit of trying to write instructions down in plain language so that the uninitiated could get an understanding of the subject but also with enough detail that will allow a seasoned engineer to learn and fill the gaps in their knowledge which naturally occur as technology develops.

This book has come about because I feel that the security industry – certainly in the UK and to my experience, globally – has a high proportion of good people with good intentions but there are so many knowledge gaps which understandably form when technology advances at the rate in which it has done in our industry. But also – and in addition to those that want to expand their knowledge – I often meet people that want to build a career in the electronic security industry who ask: 'How do I learn about integrated systems?' A good question because there are very few training courses available that cover all of the disciplines necessary to design a complete integrated scheme. Like most professions, integrated electronic security design takes both education and experience to learn all of the minute details that differentiate an appropriate and proportional scheme from one that could have severe consequences when it fails. At best, a poor design will be a waste of money; at worst it could threaten individual or national security.

This book is a starting point for those that want to enter the industry and it is a 'gap-filler' for those that are already in it. People in related industries such as facilities management, manned guarding or IT and electrical design will benefit from an understanding of how a security system works, how it is operated and the impact it can have on a building. You can read this book from cover to cover or treat it as a reference book. It has been written to educate so please use it to meet your individual needs. It draws upon my education, my many years of training and experience as well as current product research. I hope that you gain from it and use the information to add to your current skill sets but most importantly from my point of view, I hope that occasionally you respectfully correct somebody who makes a claim about something that they obviously know nothing about.

Table of Contents

 Introduction

Introduction

You may have noticed that the electronic security industry has changed significantly over the past few years. The advent of IP technology into the surveillance arena and the emergence of video analytics and wide dynamic processing have meant that a new breed of system engineer is needed to design, install and maintain a modern surveillance system. Today's integrated security engineer needs to understand computer networking and programming as well as the many facets and intricacies of deploying a surveillance system. From getting the angle of view that you want and transmitting a video signal to data analysis and evidence storage, this book explains in plain the key components and considerations that are needed to set up a successful, professional, proportional and robust integrated electronic security system.

The starting point for any integrated security scheme is to establish the Operational Requirements of the system. What is the system going to achieve? A structured risk management plan is essential to understand what the problems are and how technology is going to solve them. Modern technology allows system designers to create schemes that can seamlessly integrate with a business model so that security becomes part of the process rather than sitting on the outside of everyday life. Systems can identify and track individuals; they can even predict where and when trouble may occur. The problem today is that technology has developed faster than many system designers. The security technology industry has some very good and highly skilled individuals in it, but as products become commoditised, a whole new breed of designers is emerging who don't necessarily have all of the skills and experience needed to pull together a robust, proportional and fit-for-purpose integrated security system. Older, more experienced security engineers need to keep up with

1

technological developments and the new breed need to understand the basic principles of system deployment.

All of this means that some new skills are required for today's security engineer. The right questions need to be asked and decisions need to be made to ensure that the ensuing system design meets the intended operational requirement which initiated the project in the first place. What resolution does the CCTV system need to be? What lighting conditions will the cameras face? How secure do doors need to be? Where will data be stored and how will it get there? Should the system be converged with an existing IT infrastructure? etc. etc.

But before tackling all of the new developments within the electronic security industry, there is need for a basic understanding of the principles of image capture, data transmission and how to put together a system design from concept to delivery. IT skills are essential but are often wasted if the fundamentals are missed. This book is laid out in a way that guides you through the essentials of an integrated security system design and explains, in everyday and plain language, what each element is and why it is important. The book also introduces system terminology, some jargon, and some of the many acronyms used by seasoned professionals and, all too often, by those that don't really know what they are talking about. This book came about with an aim to cut through some of the industry sales hype by describing in everyday language the various technical aspects of designing a security system. It cannot claim to remove all of the terminology and jargon because the industry has built its own language pulled together from electronic principles, optics and network transmission. It does tackle each term as it is introduced and explains the concepts that gave rise to the jargon. This book is a guide to the language of security design as well as a knowledge base for designers, engineers, vendors and buyers alike. The language of the integrated electronic security industry is vast and forever evolving. For convenience, a Glossary of Terms has been included towards the back of this book.

The first section of the book, which is called 'Designing a CCTV System', is a summary of the major components and influences that make up a video surveillance scheme. Most importantly, it introduces the concept of operational requirements. This is the idea that the starting point for any security system is to understand and document what the issues are, if they can be resolved using technology, and how this will be achieved. This fundamental information is the backbone of the design process and it is referred to throughout the book.

The main body of the book is broken down into manageable sections which describe the architecture of each system and delve into the detail of the various types of equipment currently available. The text highlights some of the key points to consider when designing a system. These fundamentals are often missed by the inexperienced practitioner, and when mixed with ill-matched technology, it is a recipe for disaster. Time and again, this results in a system that does not fulfill its original intention. These systems waste time, money and serve little purpose in increasing safety or reducing crime.

This book goes on to describe the commissioning processes of the various systems and the ongoing maintenance to ensure that a system continues to meet its operational requirements for years to come. Each of the devices discussed here is a subject in its own right and we would be here forever if we tried to delve too deeply into the technology behind each one. The intention is to provide a high-level guide to the usual system components and introduce a few new ones for consideration rather than explore the infinite detail of the physics, electronics and theorems behind the technology.

The following sections cover a wide range of technologies that can be integrated into a whole scheme but closed circuit television is dwelt upon in detail because it is the 'eyes' of the system and often one of the most misunderstood elements. Verification is critical to an integrated system and visual verification is one of the best methods to confirm what is going on and provide indisputable evidence after the event.

Chapter

1

Operational Requirements

Before considering the design and implementation of a CCTV system, or indeed any security system, it is important to understand what the problem is that you want to solve and whether technology is the most appropriate solution. Going through the process of producing an Operational Requirements document will ensure that the key points of what is to be achieved from a new security system are considered, such as "Why do I want CCTV, do I really need it, what is its purpose, what will it achieve, what will the performance criteria be?"

A standard Operational Requirements document for a CCTV system has two distinct parts. The first part is a report on the general need for security. It is a high level report designed to identify the need, who the stakeholders are and whether CCTV is the best solution. The second report is a more detailed requirement for the system containing the specific conditions at each position of the area to be protected. This report will detail what the security measures are at each location and what the specific objectives are for individual items of equipment. The generation of an Operational Requirements document can be represented in a simplified flow chart.

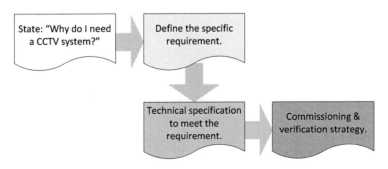

Figure 1 Operational Requirement Flow Diagram

The first part of the document defines the problem and assesses the potential impact that CCTV will have upon it, i.e. will the introduction of CCTV alleviate the problem? The report should be based upon a risk and threat analysis that has determined that the problem exists and the extent of impact should the problem occur. The problem must be clearly identified and defined; stakeholders must be consulted and the success criteria must also be documented so that a controlled and measured analysis can be carried out after the introduction of the system. This report, when complete, will clearly define the problem and the solution.

This first-stage evaluation of the need for CCTV should also address any legal and privacy issues that the introduction of a system may give rise to. The legalities of owning and using a CCTV system vary from country to country but generally they fall within data protection and privacy laws. The collection and storage of electronic data that can be used to identify an individual must be processed fairly and within the law. There must be a genuine reason for collecting the information and the data collected must not be excessive or stored for any longer than is necessary.

In European countries, the use of CCTV has to be considered in relation to the Protection of Freedom of individuals and their right to respect for private and family life. Guidance for designing a system in relation to privacy states that the system should always balance protection of the public with the rights of an individual. To assess the impact of a CCTV system on privacy of individuals, it may be necessary to carry out a separate Privacy Impact Assessment (PIA). A PIA seeks to identify the project's impact on privacy by going through a process of defining the project outline and assessing the impact through consultation and analysis. The privacy issues are then documented and reviewed before a decision to proceed is made.

The second stage of the Operational Requirements document process defines the specific requirements at each location within the area to be protected. For example, a camera is required to be sited in the rear yard to observe people at the gate. This camera must be able to monitor people in the area and see in low-light conditions because the yard lighting is reduced after midnight.

Five surveillance categories have been suggested to describe the operational performance of each of the CCTV cameras proposed within the OR.

Monitor and Control – A person occupies at least 5% of the overall CCTV image height. This level of coverage allows an operator to view across a wide area and, providing that the operator knows that they are there, it should be possible to determine the number and direction of travel of the people within the field of view.

Detect – A person occupies at least 10% of the overall CCTV image height. At 10%, it is considered that an operator can determine with a good level of accuracy that a person is in the field of view. This level of coverage is often used as verification for another detection system such as a perimeter intrusion detection system (PIDS). Once verified, an operator can dispatch the appropriate response.

Observe – A person occupies at least 25% of the overall CCTV image height. Observation provides an operator with the ability to establish the characteristics of a person. It also allows the operator to assess the behaviour of the person in context with the surroundings.

Recognise – A person occupies at least 50% of the overall CCTV image height. It is considered that if a person fills at least 50% of the screen height it is possible to establish if that person is known to the operator.

Identify – A person occupies at least 100% of the overall CCTV image height. If the Operational Requirement of the camera dictates that it is necessary to identify an unknown individual passing through a doorway for example, then it is recommended that the person fills at least 100% of the screen. This means that as much detail as possible is captured but there will be little information relating to the surrounding area.

7

Operational Requirements

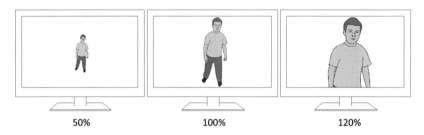

50%   100%   120%

Figure 2 CCTV Surveillance Categories

This second stage of the document, which is usually referred to as the Level 2 OR, also details the operational issues and related standard operating procedures necessary to achieve the desired results

5%R	*=*	*Monitor & Control*
10%R	*=*	*Detect*
25%R	*=*	*Observe*
50%R	*=*	*Recognise*
100%R	*=*	*Identify*

from the system. This means that consideration should be given to who monitors the system, where and when. The quality and duration of the recorded archive must also be established and high-level Standard Operational Procedures (SOPs) produced to determine the appropriate response to any given scenario. It is important to establish a method of transmitting these standard procedures to the security team to ensure that the correct response is initiated, bearing in mind that some scenarios will be rare and procedures may be forgotten.

With a complete understanding of what is required, the third step of the Operational Requirement document is to define a technical performance specification for the required CCTV equipment. This will need a good knowledge of each component of the system and an understanding of the various settings that each component has. This is important to ensure that the system can achieve the specific requirements.

Finally, the Operational Requirements document should detail the expectation for commissioning and verification of the installed system. This will ensure that the final product has been deployed as

8

specified to meet the requirements. This section can also be used to measure the technical performance of the system after it has been installed and at regular intervals in the future.

With a complete OR in place, it will then be necessary to pull together all of the components of the CCTV system to meet the requirements of your document. A good knowledge of the system architecture options and of all of the various technologies that can make up a system is essential.

> *Before considering the design and implementation of a security system, it is important to understand what the problem is that you want to solve and whether technology is the most appropriate solution.*

Chapter
2

Closed Circuit Television

Often, when discussing a CCTV system, an engineer refers to resolution. Traditionally this is about the number of television (TV) lines that make up the moving picture. However, with the introduction of digital image capture systems, resolution is now all about pixel density. The security, photographic and home video industries are working towards standards of resolution and refer to the devices as High Definition and mega-pixel cameras. Some surveillance camera manufacturers are expanding image resolution by developing systems that capture multiple images taken from a super high resolution camera made up from multiple image sensors. These 'super cameras' combine each image to make a single picture and then allow the operator to zoom into it and view a separate video stream from the near field and from far away, simultaneously. As an example, this type of technology is ideal for monitoring a crowd in a stadium where the operators can have an overview of the seating areas while still being able to identify individuals anywhere within the audience. Another relatively recent development is wide dynamic processing which allows the camera to see light and dark areas as a usable video within the same image. Before the introduction of wide dynamic processing, manufacturers concentrated on low-light performance but although valuable, low-light performance does not necessarily produce good images. This technology has developed the ability to view light and dark areas equally well within the same field of view. For example, a camera looking at a lorry yard during the day will probably have a good even-light level to help produce the video images but at night it is a very difference scene. The yard will be illuminated so that low-light capability is probably not needed within the camera. More important is the ability to cope with the different intensities and colours of the flood-lighting and the headlights of the vehicles. Amber warning beacons flashing and dark shadows created by moving and parked vehicles as they block the

11

artificial illumination add to the technical challenges of capturing good video images. Video archiving and data retrieval have moved from Video Cassette Recorders to Digital Video and then to Networked Video Recorders (NVRs) and now a system can be sitting within a virtualised computer environment, archiving to a Storage Area Network which may or may not be in the same building. In fact, and dependent on network capabilities, the storage medium may not even be in the same country.

Closed Circuit Television or CCTV is an electronic system that gathers video information from cameras deployed in the field and transmits the images to a specific place for processing. The system is closed circuit because it operates on a point-to-point basis as opposed to the signal being broadcast to many places indiscriminately such as a domestic television signal. The term 'CCTV' is arguably now incorrect in so far as modern CCTV systems are no longer 'closed'. Video signals can be transmitted all over the world via computer networks and be viewed many people simultaneously. CCTV systems are generally no longer just point-to-point connections. But the term 'CCTV' is maintained to describe a private video capture and transmission system.

CCTV is commonly associated with crime prevention but is also often used for safety or surveillance purposes or process monitoring in a factory. There are of course many applications for CCTV from machine watching to deep-sea research but for the purposes of this discussion, CCTV is deployed in the context of security and safety.

When designing a new CCTV system and in order to maximise the benefits of the scheme, it is important to establish some basic criteria. These will be the starting point for the system design. The first criterion is to define the problem and confirm that CCTV is the most appropriate response. It is then essential to establish the Operational Requirements (OR) of the system so that the developed scheme will fulfil its purpose. The phrase 'Operational Requirements' is often shortened to 'O R', written as 'OR'.

The OR is a document that details what the issues are and how CCTV will address them. By recording the requirements, the operation of the system is clarified. The document should take the reader through the issues to be addressed, who is affected and what is to be achieved by deploying a CCTV system. The OR document is generally split into two separate papers to allow an initial high-level statement of the problem to be identified and agreed before moving on to a more detailed description of the system and specific requirements. The basic model for an OR document will establish the following high-level information.

- A Site Plan – to identify areas of concern
- A Statement of the Problem
- Stakeholder Liaison
- Risk Assessment
- Success Criteria
- A Technical Solution.

Only when the first level OR is in place is it possible to start the system design for the most appropriate CCTV solution. The second level of the OR must locate each camera and identify an observation category for each one. An observation category captures what the camera is to achieve. For example, if the camera is to monitor the area, detect a figure or recognise a known individual. To help break this detail down, there are five suggested surveillance categories to use.

- Monitor and Control
- Detect
- Observe
- Recognise
- Identify.

The methods for measuring and establishing what each of these categories means in real terms to an operator is explained later in this book. For the operational requirement of any particular camera, it is necessary to document what it is there for. Only when the surveillance category has been established are other factors then taken into consideration such as image quality, target speed, lighting and environmental conditions etc.

Finally, for the OR, the response to the CCTV information needs to be considered. Who will monitor it, where from and will they be dedicated to the task? What training do they need and are there any legal issues associated with recording images such as privacy and data protection legislation?

With the Operational Requirements for the scheme in place, it is then necessary to establish the most appropriate technology to use. Does it need to be wall or ceiling-mounted, vandal-resistant, static or fully-functional? A static camera stays in a fixed position with a fixed field of view whereas a fully-functional camera can be moved left and right, up and down and zoomed in and out either automatically to respond to an alarm or manually by an operator. Questions about challenging lighting conditions such as coloured light, low light or high-contrast lighting areas must be asked. The details of how to capture all of this information is contained within the next section.

Dependant on the camera choice, a suitable lens must be selected. What size of lens is required to achieve the surveillance category detailed in the OR? The focal length of the lens affects the amount of magnification. A higher focal length has a narrow field of view but it will be zoomed in over a greater distance whereas a low number focal length lens will have a wide angle of view but very little depth to the image. Does the lens need to be IR-cut to work with infrared illumination? There are many types of illumination from sunlight through to infrared light that is not visible to the naked eye. Some of these different lighting conditions need specialised lenses, such as infrared (IR). Images under this light can appear out of focus if the camera is set up for daytime operation and switches to infrared illumination at night unless a specially adapted lens is used. This type of lens is manufactured with a slightly different shape to focus the lower frequency invisible light into the same sharp spot as the visible light.

The method of signal transmission that will most suit the Operational Requirement must be considered. For example, a choice may need to be made between fibre-optic for long distance and secure transmission or IP on a local area network for integration.

Lighting is one of the fundamentals of CCTV design. With the introduction of wide dynamic processing it is possible to get usable images in a range of challenging conditions but it is advised that the scene illumination and reflectance is understood fully to achieve the best possible results. The reflectance is the amount of light that bounces off a target that is registered by the camera. If the target for the CCTV system has a dark surface and is located within a dark area, it stands to reason that this is going to be difficult to see and therefore more illumination will be required. Conversely, if the target is highly reflective in a bright area, then less illumination is required. Ideally, a target will be reflective in a dark area or high-contrast to its surroundings, making it easily distinguishable from the background of the scene.

Display monitors must be selected to show the received images to an operator. The size and position of the monitors need to be established to enable the operator to use the system both safely and comfortably.

Finally, the recorded evidence must be established in terms of image rate, quality of compression, resolution and duration. How is the data to be exported and might it be required in a criminal case?

The summary above demonstrates that a closed circuit television system is a complicated phenomenon. Many people believe that simply putting a camera up will solve all of their problems. But without properly understanding the fundamentals of light and the intricacies of system design, it will probably be a waste of money or at best an inefficient system.

CCTV System Architecture

Closed circuit television systems are made up of numerous components; for example cameras, lenses, pan and tilt mechanisms, transmission equipment, recording devices and monitors. With the evolution of IP CCTV, systems are networked with local and wide area transmission systems. However, many systems are localised and, depending upon operational requirements, performance specification and any budgetary constraints, they are interconnected by one or several of a variety of methods including point-to-point communication such as coaxial cable, balanced signal over twisted pair or fibre-optic cables. In some instances, particularly if the infrastructure installation is difficult due to pre-existing obstacles or crossing of public areas, wireless transmission can be utilised.

The choice of transmission medium will be influenced by the operational requirements of the system. For example, if a camera is particularly sensitive or critical to the scheme, you may not want to uses wireless transmission so as to avoid signal jamming or hacking. Equally, if the cable run is in an area at risk of high electromagnetic interference then fibre-optic cable may be the best solution. The system may be a mix and match of the various transmission technologies to best suit the budget and the OR.

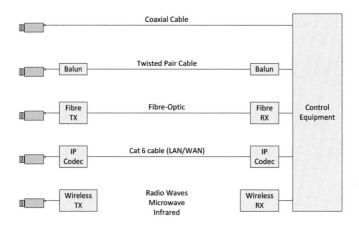

Figure 3 Video Transmission Methods

Many CCTV schemes are based on a centralised Digital Video Recording (DVR) platform. In this configuration, the field equipment – regardless of the transmission medium – connects to a digital recorder for the management of the video information. The DVR digitises and records the video signals and often has some basic management video switching capabilities such as allowing an operator to select a camera and view the images on a monitor or alarm functions that automatically switch the image to a monitor. All DVRs will allow for search of historic video and most will add some intelligence to the search by including time constraints and event activity.

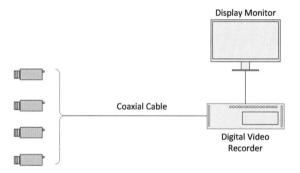

Figure 4 DVR-Controlled System

More complicated analogue systems utilise a video switching matrix to switch the video signals to a variety of display monitors dependent upon alarm activation or pre-programmed scenarios. The matrix will generally have an increased capability in telemetry function over a DVR. Telemetry is the sending and receiving of data to and from a camera receiver board. A telemetry receiver board converts the data messages from the matrix to tell the camera to either pan left or right, tilt up or down, zoom in and focus etc. A telemetry receiver board will often have the capability of switching lights on and off as well as an auxiliary control relay to switch any other device that may be connected such as detection devices. A video matrix will also usually be able to programme a number of preset positions that can be stored within the telemetry receiver board and be deployed in the event of an alarm or the initiation of a guard tour so that cameras are

17

automatically positioned to view a desired target for a predetermined period of time before either returning to a home position or proceeding to another pre-set position.

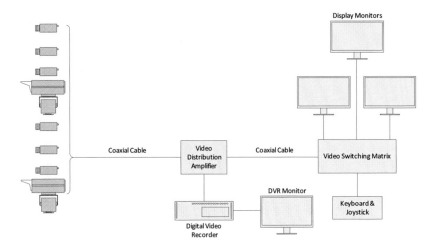

Figure 5 Matrix-Controlled System

Ultimately, the video signals are displayed on a computer screen or dedicated CCTV monitor so that an operator can make an informed decision about how to react to an event based on the information presented. Some systems display images on a video wall where the footage can be shown alongside other relevant information such as a site plan, PC application or alarm information for several operators to view simultaneously. The ability to view a lot of data on a video wall allows the security team to manage large-scale and mission critical systems efficiently.

If you are designing a scheme with a video wall then it is important to consider that if the wall uses a single display driver for all of the various inputs then this unit has the potential to be a single point of failure that could disable the control room.

IP camera systems utilise network architecture rather than the point-to-point cabling of a more traditional analogue system. With an IP camera system each device sits on a local area network which in turn can be connected to a wide area network providing the capability for cameras located all over the world to be viewed and controlled from a central 'global' control room.

A video server and virtual matrix send the TCP/IP packets of data to the relevant places for recording and display. A Networked Video Recording device (NVR) captures the images for archive, search and exporting video to a portable medium such as a DVD. The NVR is usually an array of hard disks with all of the intelligence for archive retrieval and rule-dependent searching being held on a video management server.

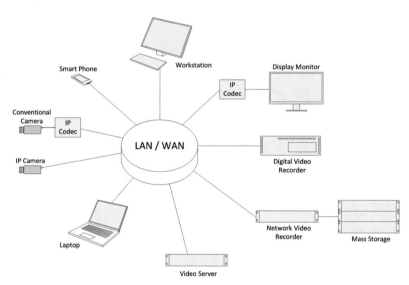

Figure 6 TCP/IP Transmission Connectivity

The field equipment for any CCTV scheme, whether IP or analogue, can be made up from a wide variety of devices that gather information, rotate a camera, provide illumination, detect unusual activity etc. The choice of field equipment is entirely dependent on the operational requirements at any given camera location. If the scene is dark all of the time then a low-light camera may be in order but if the scene has high-contrast lighting then a camera with wide dynamic functionality is called for. Detection systems will vary dependent on the environment. Windy areas where rubbish is blown around would not be suitable for the installation of a passive infrared detector because of the number of nuisance alarms that would be generated. A busy footpath would not have video motion detection for the same reason but it might have video content analysis to detect anybody straying from the path.

The final version of any closed circuit television scheme will have many components that make up the complete system architecture. The camera needs a lens at the correct focal length to achieve the desired field of view. The whole assembly will need a bracket to secure it in place and possibly an environmental housing to protect it from adverse conditions such as bad weather, dust or a corrosive atmosphere. The camera may need to be movable to allow an operator to position it with pan left and right, tilt up and down or zoom-in functions.

Whatever the camera field assembly comprises, it has to transmit the signals back to the control equipment. The transmission method may be passive or it may need a powered device such as a fibre-optic transmitter, media converter or active balun. Powered transmission technologies can send the video signal over greater distances before the image starts to break up or picks up interference. If the transmission medium has a metal content then transient suppression needs to be considered to prevent damage from induced over-voltage from lightning strikes or nearby heavy machinery.

When the video signal gets to its destination there will be a variety of control equipment devices that will be used to process the information depending on what is necessary to fulfill the operational requirements of the scheme. The whole architecture of a CCTV system is dictated by the operational requirements of the scheme, the environment, performance criteria and any budgetary constraints. However, although the list of equipment seems endless, the architecture can be simplified as shown in the following diagram.

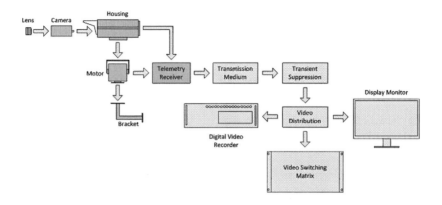

Figure 7 CCTV System Architecture

The diagram above illustrates the basic components that make up the architecture of an average CCTV system. A lens gathers the light and focuses it onto a camera sensor. The camera sits on a positioning (PTZ) motor so that it can be manually or automatically moved to view a desired scene. The whole assembly sits on a bracket to keep it in place. If a motor is used, the video signal will pass through a telemetry receiver and be transmitted to the control equipment. If the transmission medium is made up from metallic wires and they run outside or between buildings then it may be appropriate to have a transient suppression device installed to protect the control equipment from voltage spikes. The control equipment will distribute the video and process it for recording, telemetry control, switching between displays or onto a dedicated monitor.

A closed circuit television system is made up of many components that form the overall system architecture. The camera needs a lens, the assembly will possibly need an environmental housing, a transmission method will be needed and control equipment must be decided upon to process, display and record the images.

Camera Types

There are countless types of CCTV camera available today but depending on the operational requirements, the correct technology should be selected. With a CCTV camera as with any other purchase, it is important to understand the feature set of any particular device so that you can ensure that you are buying what you need rather than the latest hype generated by a company trying to boost their sales.

A fixed camera in housings offers the ability to have a larger lens and a wiper to clear away rain whereas a camera in a dome looks neater and is generally cheaper due to mass marketing of 'all-in-one' solutions. The same principle applies to pan, tilt and zoom (PTZ) cameras where an overt version has the capacity to have larger lenses and bolt-on equipment such as a wiper and white light or infrared illumination that rotates with the camera. PTZ domes have the same advantages as static domes i.e. being neat and generally cheaper but they have the same disadvantages – less flexibility and limited performance if they are used in tough environmental conditions or encounter stringent operational requirements.

Colour cameras produce good usable images but they are limited by the amount of light that is available at the scene and the sensitivity of the camera. A colour camera needs a high level of light to be able to operate and reproduce true images. Many colour cameras use digital signal processing techniques that allow them to see in relatively low-light conditions but this processing has a price attached which is often the quality of the image. Digital signal processing can enhance shadowy areas but ultimately more light is needed if the average scene is too dark.

Frame integration is a technique used by some manufacturers to increase the low-light capabilities of the camera. The system overlaps the captured images to effectively multiply the amount of light available in each frame. However, this has an observable disadvantage in that the more frames that are overlapped the more blurred moving objects appear. In simple terms, more light is gathered by slowing down the image-taking process and as with standard photography, this introduces image blur. Frame integration is a relatively old technology and more advanced equipment can produce good colour images at very low light levels.

Monochrome cameras can see at much lower light levels than colour ones because they are only sensitive to luminance (brightness) and ignore chrominance (colour). Monochrome cameras are also sensitive to infrared illumination which makes them ideal for night operation. Infrared is a frequency of light that is not visible to the naked eye but can illuminate a scene for a monochrome camera. Use of infrared light means that areas can remain visually dark but have full surveillance via CCTV. This has the advantage of covert operation and illumination without producing light pollution that overspills into neighbouring areas. The advantages of colour when sufficient light is available is obvious for identification purposes but to overcome the need for a colour camera during the day and a separate monochrome camera for nighttime, colour/mono or day/night cameras have been developed that will automatically switch from one mode to the other dependent on the available light.

CCTV cameras are often categorised by their image sensors. The Charge Coupled Device or CCD chip is the sensitive plate that converts the light focused by the lens into an electrical signal for further processing. CCDs come in a range of technologies but the more basic criterion for categorising a camera is by its CCD size. This is the diagonal dimension of the receptive area of the chip. The larger the CCD chip, the more light it can gather. In closed circuit television systems, CCD chip sizes are generally $^1/_4$", $^1/_3$" or $^1/_2$". The larger chip devices usually mean that the camera is more expensive but is likely to have better performance characteristics. However, with that said, many smaller chip cameras utilise advanced technology to provide some very high-quality images.

CCD chip sizes differ for IP cameras compared to analogue technology but the same principle applies; the larger the chip the more light is gathered at the earliest opportunity which in turn provides a better image. Light is discussed later in this book because it is a subject in its own right especially when it comes to gathering reflected light for a CCTV camera. Be aware that the statement made above could be interpreted as the "more light the better". But this is not necessarily the case. Light for a CCTV camera ideally needs to be a broad-spectrum white light that matches the frequency response of the camera and at an optimum level for processing. It is not the case of simply 'the brighter the better'. This is another reason why just putting a camera up probably won't solve your problems.

The resolution of a CCTV camera is one of the keys to its performance and that of the system overall. Resolution is the measurement of the picture quality in terms of how much electronic information is gathered from the scene. An analogue CCTV camera measures its resolution in Television Lines (TVL). These horizontal scans make up the video signal. The more horizontal scans there are in the image, the more detail the system captures and the clearer the resultant picture. The resolution of a camera, whether analogue or IP, is directly related to the number of pixels within the CCD chip. A low-resolution camera would typically be around 330 TVL and a high-resolution camera would be from 480 to 540 TVL. IP camera resolutions are discussed later in this book because they differ from analogue in two fundamental ways – aspect ratio and size. The advent of IP has also seen the advent of mega-pixel technology.

CCTV cameras also vary in the amount of processing that they can apply to the image before transmitting it to the control equipment. A high-quality camera would have a range of processing features such as backlight compensation which reduces the effect of silhouetting and automatic gain control to boost the video signal when light levels drop. For more demanding fields of view there are features that allow manual override of the shutter speed and processing circuits. Wide dynamic processing allows the camera to produce high-quality images in challenging conditions such as high-contrast lighting produced by spotlights but beyond conventional CCTV. For true night vision there are thermal imaging cameras which detect very low heat sources and display the images in a useable format. Again, these are discussed later in this book.

Static Domes

When referring to CCTV cameras, 'static' means that once installed the camera is in a fixed position. This is sometimes referred to as 'fixed line'. The camera cannot be moved by remote control to be repositioned such that it can target a particular scene. Static domes are circuit-board-mounted cameras housed within a polycarbonate protective dome. The dome offers a good level of protection for the camera inside from the weather, tampering or vandalism. These cameras can usually be either wall or ceiling-mounted with an internal gimbal to adjust the camera and lens to achieve the desired field of view. Once the field of view is set it can be locked off so that it is not inadvertently moved.

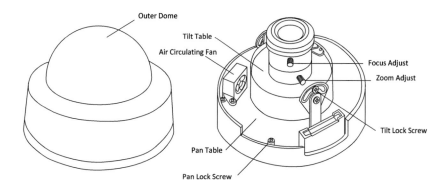

Figure 8 Simplified Static Dome Assembly

A combination of a smoked dome and a black plastic inner dome offers a visual screen so that the position and direction of the camera cannot be easily determined from afar. For this reason, these units are often referred to as covert domes. The protective domes can be clear, smoked, chromed or gold-coloured depending on the level of covert qualities and aesthetics required. A point to note is that the quality of the polycarbonate dome could affect the quality of the image. Any irregularities in the optical areas of the dome will bend the light travelling through it and cause a distortion to the image. The density of the smoke effect or reflective surface can also affect the quality of the picture. Setting up a sharp, clear image without the dome cover can sometimes result in an out-of-focus image with the cover in place. This is because when the cover is put in place the amount and sometimes the frequency of light hitting the lens changes. The phenomenon is explained further in the lens section of this book.

Static dome cameras are relatively small and are generally $^1/_4$" or $^1/_3$" monochrome, colour or colour/mono CCD format devices. Although static dome cameras can be vandal-resistant and aesthetically pleasing, they do not have the flexibility of an overt camera. For example, you cannot fit a sun shield to reduce glare in the dome and they often do not have the capabilities of a specifically designed housing such as a wash/wipe or environmental control.

Overt Static (Box Camera)

The operational requirements for the system may dictate that overt static cameras are necessary. This style of camera is often selected because there are some additional features that do not lend themselves to a static dome.

With an overt unit, a standard camera is fitted into an environmentally-controlled housing that protects the electronics and the optics from dust, adverse weather and temperature etc. In more unusual installations, the housing can also protect the camera from electromagnet interference and corrosive atmospheres. The overt camera is more suited to mounting a light fitting on the same bracket so that the beam of light can be matched to the field of view of the camera. An overt camera can have a sun shield fitted to reduce the glare on bright days especially when there is a low sun or a light source immediately above the unit.

Overt cameras frequently have more advanced functionality than dome cameras. An overt camera does not have the limitations of space that a static dome camera has and can therefore pack in more electronics.

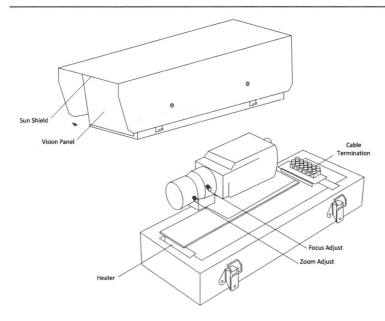

Sun Shield

Vision Panel

Cable
Termination

Focus Adjust

Zoom Adjust

Heater

Figure 9 Overt Camera Assembly

PTZ Domes

Fully-functional dome cameras offer the same covert, vandal-resistant and aesthetic qualities as the static domes but with the obvious difference of having remote-controlled pan, tilt and zoom functions. These units also offer the same colour and colour/mono options for varying lighting conditions as their static counterparts. They usually have variable speed capability and can zoom in around 18 times with the lens optical drive and with a further digital zoom potential. Be aware that the digital zoom does not zoom the image in any further, it simply enlarges the pixels electronically. This may result in image degradation. Many PTZ domes have video stabilisation circuitry that reduces the effects of vibration on the image. Another common feature on PTZ domes is auto focus as the camera zooms in so that there is always a sharp image when an operator controls the dome. It is quite rare to get these technologies in an overt camera.

PTZ domes usually have 360° of variable speed and constant rotation with maximum speeds in the region of 80° per second panning and 40° per second tilting. These figures are for when an operator is controlling the device. The speed to deploy an automated preset position can be in the region of 400° per second pan and 150° per second tilt. The dome incorporates a number of these individually programmable preset positions which will deploy the camera to the same position every time an instruction to do so is received. Preset deployment can be from an alarm signal received directly at the dome or can also be via an external integrated device such as a movement detector, from an instruction by an operator or as part of a sequence of preset positions known as a tour. A tour can be timed so that the camera moves to preset position one – a door for example – and stays there for 30 seconds. After the 30 seconds has elapsed the dome will move to preset position two which may be a roadway and stay there for a different predetermined time and so on. Tours allow a PTZ camera to cover multiple views over a given period of time. The biggest disadvantage of any PTZ camera is that it can only see in the direction it is pointing which means that it is ideal for a reactive system where the camera will deploy either automatically or manually to an event. However, it is limited for a passive evidence gathering system because it could be looking in the wrong direction when the event occurs.

PTZ domes come in a variety of mounting types so that they can be installed indoors or outdoors, on a pendant hanging down or fitted into the underside of a canopy or into a ceiling for a more discreet installation.

> *Any equipment that is mounted at height should have a lanyard attached. In this case, a lanyard is a chain or wire that connects to the body of the camera assembly and to the structure of the building that it is mounted on. The lanyard is a safety device to ensure that the equipment cannot fall and injure somebody.*

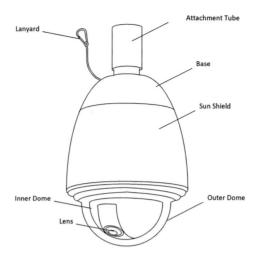

Figure 10 PTZ Dome Assembly

Overt PTZ

An overt pan, tilt and zoom camera has the potential for a more flexible design. The unit is a combination of equipment dependent upon the operational requirements. In its basic form, a conventional CCTV camera is mounted within an environmental housing that sits upon a pan and tilt motor that will rotate the unit through a full 360° and tilt it straight up or straight down. A telemetry receiver board controls the assembly for the pan, tilt and zoom functions. Signals are received from the control system that directs the camera to move left or right, up or down, zoom in or zoom out. The flexibility of an overt PTZ comes from the ability to add a combination of camera, lens, environmental housing, wash-wipe, illumination etc. all dependent on what the cameras is trying to achieve.

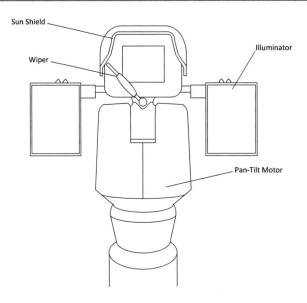

Figure 11 Overt PTZ Assembly

A typical pan-tilt motor can support a 12-kilogram load providing that it is correctly balanced. The motor will rotate up to and around 40° per second but the tilt speed is usually slower at almost half that of the rotation. There are two types of motor each with many variants but fundamentally a motor is either ac controlled or dc controlled. An ac-controlled motor will only move at a constant speed but a dc-controlled one has variable speed control from zero to maximum speed dependent on the amount of pressure applied to the controlling joystick.

Many pan and tilt motors are able to rotate constantly in one direction without having to stop and go back the other way. This is made possible by a set of slip rings mounted in the base of the unit which allow the control and video signals to pass through the motor without the need for a loop of cable that would tangle after a single rotation. However, it not always necessary or desirable to have constant rotation on a PTZ camera. This could be because there is a nearby residential area or school for example which would not appreciate a camera looking into its area. Limit switches are often provided to ensure that the camera does not rotate past a mechanically-set position so ensuring privacy in this region of the rotation. Although electronic privacy zones can be deployed, a mechanical stop – also known as an end stop – ensures that the camera never points towards the private area. This has the benefit of reducing complaints from neighbours because when electronic privacy zones are deployed the camera can still point at the private area even though the masking obscures the picture so giving the perception that privacy is being compromised.

Some PT motors are available which retain constant rotation but have circuitry built in that stops the camera from pointing in any predefined direction. These 'electronic' or 'virtual' limit switches make the camera move around a private area rather than through it. This avoids the sensitive issue of a camera potentially looking in a direction in which it should not.

Electronic privacy zones are set up within the camera assembly receiver board. Electronic privacy is a means of masking regions of the field of view on the displayed camera image. The motor and lens contain devices that measure their coordinate location by a voltage level set through a potentiometer that moves as the assembly moves. This information feeds back to the telemetry receiver board so that it can place a masked area over the image when pre-programmed positions are recognised.

Figure 12 Electronic Privacy Zones

The image in Figure 12 is of a VIP parking area at the front of a prestigious hotel. The camera view is observing people around the vehicles but viewing the windows of adjacent buildings is unavoidable. The operational requirement of the camera does not include viewing through these windows so they are electronically masked from the scene.

The telemetry receiver board is the part of the PTZ camera assembly that receives instructions from the control system to tell the unit to pan, tilt, zoom, focus etc. The signals are received via a separate data cable or sometimes embedded within the video signal and received through the coaxial cable. The data has a set protocol which is the language that the receiver can understand from the control equipment. Many telemetry receiver boards have the ability to select different protocols so that they can communicate with a wide range of control equipment. This allows a system to use equipment from different manufacturers which is a distinct advantage when designing a CCTV scheme.

As well as the pan, tilt and zoom functions, the receiver board can provide a range of auxiliary functions. Alarm inputs allow preset positions to be deployed in response to a local signal. Privacy zones are programmed and stored within the receiver board so that sections of the video signal are blanked out dependent on the position of the motor and lens. Auxiliary outputs can be used to switch additional devices such as wipers, lights or sounders.

The main advantage of the overt PTZ assembly is the flexibility of build. Large lenses, wash and wipe functions and various other additional equipment can be added to the assembly. A heavy-duty motor can support the camera in its housing along with bolt-on lighting that rotates with the camera. This ensures that the field of view is always illuminated wherever the camera is pointing. PTZ-mounted light fittings are often deployed in pairs consisting of a wide-angled floodlight to illuminate the near ground and a narrow spotlight to illuminate the scene in the distance. Note: it is important to match the illumination to the lens. For example, if the camera has been designed to see for 300 metres then a 300-metre spotlight is fitted to provide the distance illumination.

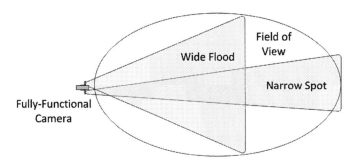

Figure 13 PTZ Illumination Configuration

A good quality heavy-duty PT motor can support a conventional CCTV camera as well as light fittings and a thermal imaging camera for more demanding conditions. This combination gives a clear colour image during the day, a monochrome image in low light and a thermal image that can see through the dark, rain and fog. The combinations of equipment available for an overt PTZ camera make it ideal for wide area surveillance and similar challenging tasks.

Another point to note is that powerful zoom lenses deployed to see targets that are over a long distance – for example a kilometre away – need to have a very accurate PT motor. To demonstrate this: suppose that we have a motor with 0.1% degree accuracy. This is fine when viewing across a scene that is only a few tens of metres from near to far because any inaccuracies will only show up as a few centimetres of error. But a 0.1% degree error over a kilometre distance can result in an error factor in the region of 1.6m off-target at the scene. This means that preset positions will not necessarily return to the same place every time. Viewing over these distances also means that every vibration is amplified at the scene so a very accurate and stable PT motor is required. There are specialised PT motors available where accuracy is increased to 0.01% degree using patented designs or Harmonic Wave Drive Motors. Both systems have a highly engineered mechanism that allows for more accurate and smooth positioning with near-zero backlash compared to a standard PT motor.

Conventional CCTV Cameras

The conventional CCTV camera sits at the heart of the field equipment whether it is an overt pan, tilt and zoom or a static camera within an environmental housing. The conventional 'box' camera describes any camera that is not built into a specialised housing such as a dome or 'bullet' style housing. Many of the functions described in the next few paragraphs relating to a conventional camera also relate to static dome and PTZ dome units. However, the difference is that a conventional CCTV camera allows the system designer more flexibility in putting together the scheme to meet the performance specification. These standard cameras can be matched up with zoom lenses, environmental housings and pan/tilt motors etc. to best suit the environment and operational requirements dictated by the performance specification.

The following features allow the cameras to operate in difficult lighting conditions. Generally, conventional cameras have more flexibility in manually adjusting these features.

Auto Iris lens control is a system that uses the camera processing to mechanically open and close the iris of the lens so that the amount of light hitting the CCD chip is regulated to provide optimum performance. Conventional CCTV cameras offer two types of auto iris control. Auto Iris (AI) control is used for lenses that contain their own signal amplifier. The amplifier converts the video signal from the camera into a control voltage that drives the motor to open and close the iris within the lens. A Direct Drive (DD) control signal is for a lens that does not contain its own amplifier to process the video signal. With this system, the processing takes place within the body of the camera and the control voltage is sent directly to the lens motor hence 'Direct Drive'.

Automatic gain control (AGC) is a feature whereby an internal signal amplifier maintains the video signal under varying lighting conditions. As the scene gets darker the AGC automatically increases the sensitivity. The down side to this is that an AGC amplifier will also increase the amount of noise in a signal as it tries to boost the image in very low light conditions. Automatic gain control is provided in addition to the camera's standard gain which is not adjustable since it is integral to the camera's internal signal processing. AGC provides extra flexibility under varying lighting conditions but don't be afraid to turn it off to reduce noise in the image if lighting levels are too low.

Backlight compensation is an electronic circuit that makes an assumption as to which element of the scene is the target and optimises the light levels for this area. This circuit will remove the silhouetting effect caused by intense light from behind the target. This feature is ideally suited to internal cameras looking at an external door to view people entering a space, especially if it is a glass door similar to one you would find in a shop. The camera will shut down its iris and gain control to view through the glass door when it is closed but as soon as somebody enters and that element of the scene goes dark, the camera will compensate and lighten the image to view the person rather than outside. With backlight compensation the brighter area behind the target will 'white out' as the camera allows more light in to capture the scene. However, Wide Dynamic Processing (WDR) within the Digital Signal Processing (DSP) takes scene illumination management to a different level. (You may have noticed that wide dynamic processing is referred to by manufacturers as WDR which stands for Wide Dynamic Range).

Wide Dynamic Digital Signal Processing is the camera's ability to take the raw video information and process it to enhance the image for better clarity. The prefix 'Wide' refers to the range of processing that the camera is able to achieve while 'Dynamic' refers to the fact that it is constantly changing. The electronic circuits take a single video frame and integrate it with adjacent frames to calculate the optimum performance. The result is a video signal that can produce good quality images under a wide range of lighting conditions. This is the technology that allows a camera to clearly see light and dark areas simultaneously in the same scene. DSP is more than just backlight compensation which sacrifices one light level to optimise another. DSP can help the camera to see at very low light levels and capture a usable image from a high-contrast scene such as floodlights in a yard. Wide dynamic processing within the DSP is the camera's ability to adjust to varying light conditions within the individual video frame. Each pixel of the frame is processed so that light and dark areas within the same field of view are balanced to provide a clear image across the scene. Wide dynamic processing is one of the most useful features on a CCTV camera that is located in challenging lighting conditions.

The electronic shutter feature is the camera's own ability outside of the lens to compensate for low or intense lighting conditions. A high-speed shutter setting is used for intensely illuminated areas and a low-speed setting is used for darker areas. Electronic shutters can be manually set to a single lighting condition which is ideal for an internal location or set to automatic for varying conditions such as an external position. Automatic shutter adjustment is also useful when the camera is used with a pan and tilt motor so that it can automatically adjust as it pans through light and dark scenes. But bear in mind that just as with standard photography, a slow shutter speed will introduce motion blur and although this may sometimes be a good photographic effect it is not often desirable within a CCTV image.

Colour/Monochrome Cameras

The human eye registers light in the 'visible light' spectrum which ranges from about 400 to 700 nanometres (nm). The sensitivity that a camera has to any particular frequency of light is known as its spectral response. For example, one model of camera may be slightly more sensitive to yellow light and another more sensitive to blue light but generally, a conventional colour CCTV camera will register light within the same visible spectrum as the human eye. However, a monochrome camera only needs brightness (luminance) to display the grayscales of an image; it is not interested in the colour (chrominance) element of the light. This means that a monochrome camera can see beyond the visible light spectrum and see the brightness levels within the infrared (IR) spectrum. This capability allows a monochrome camera to see in zero visible light with supporting infrared illumination.

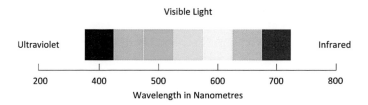

Figure 14 The Light Spectrum

Colour/monochrome (usually shortened to colour/mono or day/night) cameras capture the best of both worlds by utilising a colour image when there is sufficient visible light, either during the day or under white light illumination, and then switching to monochrome when the levels of visible light drop. These cameras can produce good quality images through the visible light spectrum and beyond to about 1250nm which is known as infrared light.

A colour/mono camera automatically switches from day to night mode, or colour to monochrome, when it measures that there is insufficient white light to maintain the colour image. At this point the camera mechanically moves an infrared filter away from the CCD chip to allow as much non-visible light as possible to hit the sensor. This filter is in place during the day because infrared light is apparent during the day and it produces grey scales within the image which affect the colour representation. Having the filter in place reduces the amount of infrared light that the CCD receives during the day to allow the camera to provide high-quality colour images.

To get good quality images, colour/mono cameras must be used with IR-corrected lenses that can focus the infrared light when the filter is not in place. Without an IR-corrected lens fitted, the image would be

37

slightly out of focus in either night or day mode. This is known as focus shift. There is more about the phenomenon later in this book.

EMCCD Cameras

Electron Multiplying Charge Coupled Device (EMCCD) cameras use a technology that operates at very low light conditions when compared to a normal CCD camera. The EMCCD sensor is capable of detecting a single photon event in a laboratory by using a unique electron multiplying structure built into the chip. When this technology is deployed in a CCTV camera it produces a device that can provide good quality images through bright light in the day and from scenes during an overcast but starlit night without additional illumination. EMCCD cameras are around 100 times more sensitive than a standard CCD device.

Thermal Imaging

Thermal imaging cameras only detect the infrared element of the light spectrum which is emitted as very low levels of heat from people and objects at the scene. The camera turns these heat levels into gray-scale video for transmission into the closed circuit television system.

The infrared light is focused onto an array of detector elements which generate a detailed pattern of the received light known as a thermogram. This thermogram is converted into an electrical signal for processing and onward transmission to the control and monitoring equipment.

Thermal imaging cameras fall into one of two categories – cooled or un-cooled. Generally the cameras used for CCTV purposes are un-cooled which means that they work at ambient temperatures and do not have any onboard cooling mechanism. A cryogenically-cooled camera has an inbuilt cooling mechanism that allows for a greater level of sensitivity to heat detection. These cameras can provide far more detailed images than their cheaper counterparts.

Whether the camera is cooled or un-cooled, the thermal imaging technology is not dependent on visible light and can therefore see clearly in the dark or through challenging weather conditions.

Figure 15 Thermal Imaging

Image: credit GC^2 Associates Ltd.

The thermal image in figure 15 was taken on a sunny day. The sensor is picking up the heat reflected from the building in the top right and a shadow is cast from the adjacent building on the left. The shadows look just like light shadows but they are in fact where the surface temperature is slightly lower than the areas that are warmed by the sun.

The higher temperature areas are displayed with a greater luminosity, i.e. brighter in the grey-scale. This is demonstrated by the heat given off beneath the lorry and the forklift truck. The same luminosity clearly picks out the driver of the forklift.

IP Cameras

An IP camera gathers the video information in the same way as any conventional camera but the fundamental difference between an IP camera and conventional CCTV is in the transmission method.

Outside of this, an IP camera should not function any differently to a standard analogue CCTV camera. An IP camera has a built-in video server which provides a unique IP address that allows it to be detected and to communicate with a computer via a TCP/IP network in the same way as any other computer network device. The transmission network can be either local (LAN) or a wide area network (WAN) meaning that the IP camera is not limited by the location of the control equipment. IP cameras have the capability to be monitored either locally or from thousands of miles away.

The control equipment for an IP CCTV system is a computer or server that communicates with one or with multiple IP cameras streaming the video data to hard disks for archiving and to monitor screens for display.

IP cameras often take advantage of the Power over Ethernet (PoE) standards that allow the power for the camera to be transmitted on the same cable as the IP signal. This technology removes the need for a separate low-voltage power supply and mains power connection so making installation a lot easier and often more cost-effective.

The resolution of an IP camera image is measured in the number of rows of pixels at the CCD sensor. IP cameras have a range of resolution sizes from standard definition (SD) at around 480 to 576 rows of pixels to high definition (HD) at around 720 to 1080 rows of pixels. 720p is regarded as equivalent to one mega-pixel and 1080p is regarded as equivalent to a two mega-pixel camera.

The resolution of Standard Definition IP cameras is expressed in terms of Common Intermediate Format (CIF)

Expression	H x V Array	Pixel Count
QCIF	176 x 120	21,120
CIF	352 x 240	84,480
2CIF	704 x 240	168,960
4CIF	704 x 480	337,920
16CIF	1280 x 1024	1,310,720

Figure 16 Resolution Table

Beyond HD, mega-pixel cameras are measured in the number of pixels available which is commonly between three and five mega-pixels. Even higher resolution cameras are available for monitoring very large areas in detail with a single camera.

One of the great advantages of IP CCTV systems is the processing applications available to enhance the system. Mega-pixel cameras can be used to provide multiple images from a single camera. A software application running on the main video server can split a camera image that has a high pixel density into four or more, lower resolution images. This technology gives the operator the ability to select 'virtual' cameras from within the system. There is more about this type of processing in the 360° and Panoramic Mega-pixel Cameras Section later in the book.

When considering IP cameras it is important to understand the implications of aspect ratio. Aspect ratio is the shape of the video image. Conventional CCTV and SD IP cameras usually have an aspect ratio of 4:3. This means that for every four units of measurement horizontally there are three of the same unit vertically. For example if the image is 48 centimetres wide, it must be 36 centimetres high to be 4:3 ratio. By contrast, a 16:9 aspect ratio image is wide-screen format where if it is 48 centimetres wide, it must only be 27 centimetres high. This aspect ratio difference must be considered when selecting the display monitors for either SD or HD cameras. If there is a mismatch in display monitor and camera there will be black bars at the top and bottom or at either side of the screen. It is possible to remove these black bars by either zooming into the image or distorting it to fit the monitor. Neither is desirable; the correct display monitor should be used to maintain the aspect ratio of the image.

Raw video data is very large in network terms so to transmit and store it in an efficient way the IP camera compresses the data into a more manageable size. There are some other techniques that will further reduce the amount of network bandwidth required such as reduced number of images per second and reduced image quality. These are both user-configurable dependent on the quality required and the amount of bandwidth available. Video compression is a digital process carried out within the IP camera. The compression aims to reduce the image file size with minimum degredation to the image quality. There are several types of compression associated with IP CCTV, the two most common formats being MPEG and H Series compression. MPEG stands for the Moving Pictures Experts Group which has been formed by the ISO (International Organisation for Standards) to set the standards for audio and video compression. The MPEG standards have evolved over time but a joint project between the Moving Pictures Expert Group and the telecommunications industry sought to find a simplified yet efficient compression technique that tackled some weaknesses in previous standards. The H.264 video compression standard was the result of this project. The Moving Pictures Expert Group call the same standard MPEG-4 Part 10/AVC. The standard met the goals of the project, providing a format for the recording and transmission of High Definition video. Video compression standards will continue to evolve and improve as manufacturers and end-users seek to challenge the current image quality and push the boundaries for large data handling.

The amount of bandwidth that an IP CCTV camera system requires from a network infrastructure is dependent on many things. Image quality, compression, images per second and the amount of activity at the scene are all factors that affect the required bandwidth. A cautionary note: be aware of the impact that an IP CCTV system can have on an existing computer network. Many existing networks are not able to cope with the large volumes of data that a CCTV system can generate. Compared to most network devices, an IP camera requires far more bandwidth on the transmission layer to maintain quality of service.

Until recently, one of the problems with using IP cameras was that as soon as a manufacturer was selected for an IP CCTV system, the end-user was tied to that manufacturer for any additional equipment. This was because each manufacturer had their own communications protocols which were not compatible with any of their competitors. Protocols are the data formats for information travelling between devices. A simple analogy is that of different languages – an English-speaking device may not understand the commands from Japanese-speaking devices therefore all devices need to speak the same language – either English or Japanese.

The Open Network Video Interface Forum (ONVIF) is a group founded in 2008 which has the sole purpose of guiding the IP CCTV industry down the route of developing products that can operate over a non-proprietary network. The aim of the group is to have interoperability across cameras, management software, storage and video analytics so that systems can be constructed from a range of products from different manufacturers. ONVIF was set up by, and has the full support of, many leading manufacturers.

360⁰ and Panoramic Mega-pixel Cameras

With the advent of mega-pixel cameras it has become possible to monitor very large areas with a single camera. By using a wide angled lens, the camera can capture a wide field of view and because of the increased pixel density it is possible to digitally zoom in to multiple areas of the field of view to create multiple CCTV images.

Figure 17 Multiple Images from a Single Mega-Pixel Image

Some manufacturers have developed software that 'stitches' the view of several cameras together so providing a mega-pixel image that is greater than that of any single camera. These clusters of cameras usually produce wide panoramic views when arranged side-by-side but at least one manufacturer has developed a system that stitches images together from cameras that are zoomed in by differing amounts of the same scene so resulting in images being combined left to right and in and out.

An example is a large car park where three cameras are set to wide angle view over the entire width of the scene but five more cameras are zoomed in to view the full width at the furthest point of the car park as well. This system provides a very large image that retains its quality as the operator digitally zooms in. Such systems are ideal in stadiums where it is important to monitor the entire scene but have the ability to digitally enhance the image to see the finest detail of an individual in the crowd. The biggest advantage of these systems over a camera that can pan, tilt and zoom to view the detail is that the systems are viewing and recording all of the information at once so that even after the event you can still zoom into the image.

Figure 18 Panoramic Image

Using a very wide angled lens – referred to as a fish-eye lens – will produce a warped image when viewed normally but if the camera is mounted on a ceiling it will capture a 360° field of view of the area. The view is difficult to interpret with the naked eye because straight lines will be curved and proportions will be distorted. De-warping software straightens these images out so that the operator can see a clear 360° panoramic view of the area. The software allows the operator to navigate and zoom into the panoramic scene while the system records the entire 360° field of view. This capability exceeds that of a fully-functional camera which can only record the field of view of the direction in which it is pointing at any given moment in time.

Figure 19 Fish-eye and Dewarped Image

Image: credit Oncam Grandeye

The All-Important Lens

The camera lens is arguably the most important part of a CCTV system given the fact that without the ability to correctly gather the light and focus it onto the CCD chip, the system would be useless no matter how good the electronics are. Selecting the best lens to achieve the operational requirement of the camera is essential to a successful system design.

In simple terms, a lens gathers the light and focuses it onto the CCD chip. The level of zoom or magnification is determined by the focal length of the lens which is the distance between the centre of the lens and the focal point. This distance is measured in millimetres and is directly related to the angle of view achieved by the lens. The greater the focal length, the more zoomed-in the image will be. A smaller focal length will result in a wider angled image. The focal point is the point where the light converges before being inverted and projected onto the CCD chip. A good quality lens will have a very tight focal point where all of the light converges for the sharpest image whereas a cheaper, poor quality lens will focus the light at slightly different points resulting in a 'soft' image.

45

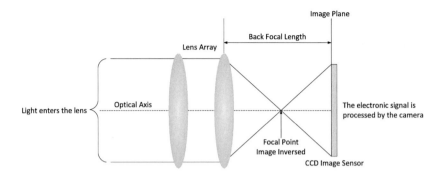

Figure 20 Simple Lens Configuration

As well as focusing the light, a lens needs to have the ability to limit the amount of light entering the camera. This is achieved with a device called an iris. The iris is adjusted to either shut down to reduce the amount of light in a bright scene or open up to let as much light in as possible in a dark scene.

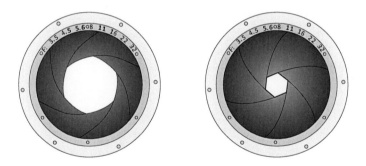

Figure 21 Simple Iris Configuration

The aperture or opening determines the cone angle of the rays of light as they enter the lens. This means that the smaller the aperture is, the more parallel the rays of light are that enter the lens and therefore the sharper the focus. The measurement units for a lens aperture are known as f-stops which are the ratio between the focal length and the effective aperture diameter.

The opening and closing of the iris aperture is either a manual operation or it is automatically controlled from the camera. There are two different types of automatic control known as either auto iris (AI) or direct drive (DD). An auto iris lens contains a small amplifier that converts the brightness in the video signal to a voltage that controls a motor to open and close the iris appropriately. The direct drive lens does not contain this amplifier as the signal is processed within the camera and the control voltages are sent directly to the motor to make the necessary changes to the iris.

Depth of field is the area of view over which the lens can provide a sharp image between a near point and a far point. In literal terms, a lens can only focus on a single location but in practical terms there is a usable image before and after the focal point. This means that a CCTV camera can view a scene over a distance rather than just a single point.

The usable depth of field is dependent on several factors: the distance from the camera to the target area, the focal length of the lens, the amount of light at the scene and the aperture of the iris. Other factors come in to play such as the amount of light entering the lens and the way that it focuses this light but generally the further away the target is from the camera and the greater the focal length of the lens, the greater the usable depth of field will be.

Understanding depth of field is important because if the operational requirement demands a large depth of field then the camera location needs to be carefully considered. However, it should be noted that the further away the camera is located from the target, the more problems there are in achieving a good quality image. The simple fact is that there is a greater distance for the camera to look across which can lead to poor image quality especially in inclement weather. Also, the more the camera is zoomed in, the more apparent vibration and movement will be in the resultant image. A small movement at the camera is amplified over distance.

Lens Formats

Not all lenses are the same. A fixed focal length lens of 12mm may not give the desired result unless it is matched to the correct CCD chip size. Lenses are manufactured to match the camera formats of $\frac{1}{4}$", $\frac{1}{3}$" and $\frac{1}{2}$" etc. This means that a $\frac{1}{4}$" format lens will not work the same on a $\frac{1}{3}$" camera.

The lens format simply applies to the amount of spread that the image has after the focal point in relation to the CCD chip. Therefore, a $\frac{1}{4}$" lens on a $\frac{1}{3}$" camera will result in dark areas around the outside of the image. Conversely, a $\frac{1}{3}$" lens will work on a $\frac{1}{4}$" camera and will theoretically give a better result because the $\frac{1}{4}$" CCD chip only receives light from the centre of the lens.

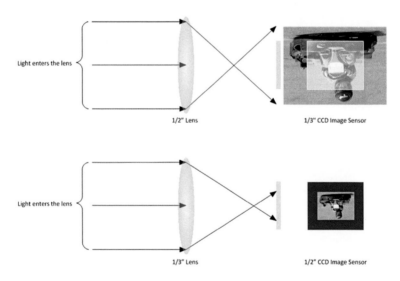

Figure 22 Mismatched Lens and Camera (Exaggerated)

The fact that a larger lens will work on a smaller format CCD chip can be misleading when calculating fields of view. For example, the horizontal angle of view of a 10mm $\frac{1}{4}$" lens on a $\frac{1}{4}$" CCD is 20.4° whereas a 10mm $\frac{1}{3}$" lens on a $\frac{1}{3}$" CCD is 27.1°. Do not fall into the trap of assuming that all 10mm lenses provide a 27.1° horizontal angle of view. Angle of view changes dependent on the focal length and the CCD size combination.

There is a second format of lens that also needs to be considered. Lenses are manufactured with two mounting types. A screw thread allows the lens to be connected to the camera body but there are two different sizes of screw thread. Both mounting types have the same diameter and pitch of thread but the difference is in the length of the thread. This difference shifts the lens approximately 5mm either away from or towards the CCD chip. This distance is referred to as the back focus.

The two types of lens mount are known as C and CS. A C mount lens has a distance of 17.5mm from the image plane of the lens to the CCD chip. This distance is 12.5mm for a CS mount lens. A C mount lens can be fitted to a CS mount camera by using a focus ring which is a 5mm spacer that fits between the lens and the camera body. Many cameras have a mechanically-adjustable spacer built in to allow for this difference. A CS mount lens will not work on a C mount camera because the image plane will always be too far from the CCD chip. A C mount lens on a CS mount camera without a focus ring could cause serious damage to the CCD chip if it were fully screwed in.

The adjustable spacer on some cameras can also be used to fine-tune the back focus which is particularly important for zoom lenses to keep them in focus throughout their zoom track.

Fixed Focus Lens

A fixed focus lens is one where the focal distance is fixed and cannot be adjusted either manually at the lens or remotely via a telemetry signal. These lenses are manufactured in a range of focal lengths to provide wide angled views at around 3mm to zoomed in narrow angle views at around 50mm. Lens sizes vary between different manufacturers; some go wider with a shorter focal length and some zoom in further.

Fixed lenses have an advantage over zoom lenses because they contain fewer optics. This means that the light has to travel through less glass to reach the CCD chip. The advantage is rarely noticeable in practice but theoretically there will be less distortion in the resulting image.

The following table illustrates the different angles of view of each focal length compared to the CCD chip size. The figures are approximate due to the number of decimal places used in the calculations. Please also remember that a fraction of a degree error in the lens calculation could equate to several metres of error in the field of view when looking over a long distance.

Focal Length	Horizontal Angle			Vertical Angle		
	$^1/_4$"	$^1/_3$"	$^1/_2$"	$^1/_4$"	$^1/_3$"	$^1/_2$"
4mm	48.5	61.9	77.3	37.3	48.5	61.9
6mm	33.4	43.6	56.1	25.4	33.4	43.6
8mm	25.4	33.4	43.6	19.2	25.4	33.4
12mm	17.1	22.6	29.9	12.8	17.1	22.6
16mm	12.8	17.1	22.6	9.6	12.8	17.1
25mm	8.2	11	14.6	6.2	8.2	11
50mm	4.1	5.5	7.3	3.1	4.1	5.5

Figure 23 Lens Comparison Chart

There is a formula that calculates the required focal length of a lens dependent on the CCD chip size, the target distance and the required scene height.

When we know the operational requirement, the scene height is the only variable in the calculation given that we know how far away the target is and what size CCD chip we are using. If the operational requirement demands that an average person fills 50% of the monitor screen for recognition purposes then we have to make an assumption on the height of the average person. Let us assume that this is 1.6m. (This is based on the Rotakin® target system used to test CCTV systems). The scene height must be 3.2m to achieve the OR (twice that of the target height).

The diagram in figure 24 shows that the reflected light hitting the CCD chip from the scene is directly proportional to the actual scene height. To achieve 50% Rotakin® we have a fixed scene height of 3.2m. If the focal length of the lens is fixed, the target will appear smaller as the distance between the camera and scene increases. However, in our example the distance is fixed and it is the focal length which we need to calculate.

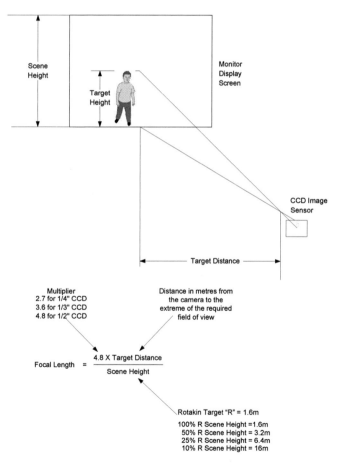

Figure 24 Rotakin Calculation

The calculation uses a 'given' multiplier that is multiplied by the target distance in metres. This sum is then divided by the required scene height which is also measured in metres. The resultant figure is the focal length of the lens needed to achieve the desired field of view. For example, if the operational requirement is to see a person 80m away at 10% of the screen height, we would do the following sum.

Let's assume that we are using a $^1/_3$" camera and that our average person is 1.6m tall. The first part of the sum is to multiply the given multiplier for a $^1/_3$" camera by the target distance.

3.6 x 80 = 288

We then divide this number by the scene height. We only need our man to be 10% of the scene height, so, if he is 1.6m tall then the scene height is 16m (1.6 being 10% of 16).

288 ÷ 16 = 18

An 18mm lens on a $^1/_3$" camera will see a person 80m away filling 10% of the monitor screen.

> *Remember: the fact that a larger lens will work on a smaller format CCD chip can be misleading when calculating fields of view. A 10mm lens on a $^1/_4$" chip will produce a different level of zoom to the same lens on a $^1/_3$" chip.*

Manual Zoom Lens

When designing a system where a range of fixed lenses is not viable, one has to turn to manual zoom lenses to get the best field of view. Most 'manual zoom' lenses are marketed as varifocal but there is a difference between these and a true manual zoom lens. A varifocal, as the name suggests, shifts its focus with every zoom adjustment. By contrast, a true manual zoom lens adjusts the optical array so that the focus is fixed to an acceptable sharpness throughout the zoom range. Elements of the optical array move either closer together or further apart as the zoom is adjusted while other elements adjust to compensate for the focal shift. A true zoom lens uses between three and five moving groups comprising up to 20 individual optics. Conversely, in a varifocal lens there is no attempt to maintain a sharp focus through mechanical or optical compensation. This results in a cheaper zoom lens with the disadvantage of not being able to maintain a constant focus throughout the zoom range.

In most applications, a varifocal lens will be adjusted and 'locked off' at the best setting to provide a permanent fixed field of view. However, in a system where each camera interacts with the next and fine adjustment of the field of view is necessary to get the optimum overlapping views, a manual zoom lens is a far more useful tool. These overlapping applications are probably not encountered very often but large, high-quality systems such as one covering the perimeter of a high-security establishment for example, may need fixed focal lengths that can only be achieved using manual zooms being finely adjusted and then locked into position. The same may apply in a casino situation or any high-value/high-stakes environment. To set up such a system with varifocal lenses would be unnecessarily difficult and time-consuming. In any CCTV system, the preference from a quality point of view would be to get the survey right, do the calculations and provide a CCTV system with fixed focus lenses.

Motor Zoom Lens

Motor zoom lenses have all the functionality of a manual zoom lens but with the ability to remotely control the zoom, focus and iris functions. This is achieved using lens drive outputs from a telemetry receiver board that connect to miniature motors which turn in order to mechanically adjust the lens. The lens contains devices that measure the coordinate location of zoom and focus by a voltage level set through a potentiometer that moves as the assembly moves. This information is fed back to the receiver board so that pre-programmed positions are recognised for either preset deployment or privacy masking.

Motor zoom lenses are usually used in conjunction with pan, tilt and zoom assemblies so that they can react to events or be manually controlled by the system operator to zoom in and follow a target.

Aspherical Lens

With an aspherical lens, the shape of the lens element is not the standard convex shape that you would find in other lenses. An aspherical lens has a more complex shape that reduces the amount of distortion in the rays of light that pass through it. The edges of an aspherical lens are less curved than a standard one which means that more light can get through. This means that an aspherical lens produces a better quality image at lower light levels.

IR-Corrected Lens

When light passes through a solid object such as glass, the different frequencies refract or bend at very slightly different angles. This is what causes the rainbow effect when white light is sent through a prism. The white light enters the prism and when each colour (frequency) bends at a slightly different angle, the individual colours appear separately out of the other side.

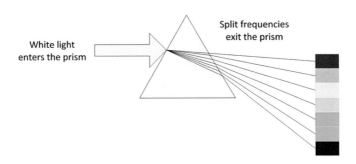

Figure 25 Light Refraction

The reverse angles of refraction occur through a convex lens which will focus the light to a single point. There is minor distortion at the focal point known as the blur spot. This is due to each frequency of light hitting the focal point at a very slightly different angle but it does not impact on the usable quality of the image. However, when the scene is illuminated by infrared (IR) light for night vision, the angle at which the IR light bends through the lens is so far off the focal point of the white light that picture degradation occurs.

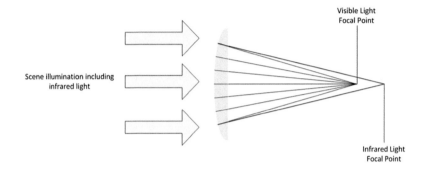

Figure 26 IR Light Passing Through a Standard Lens

This condition is known as focus shift. It occurs when images that are sharp under one lighting condition are blurred under another. It can be noticeable between daylight and artificial light so that a camera that is in focus on a scene such as a goods yard during the day becomes out of focus at night when the floodlights are turned on. This difference can usually be compensated for by fine adjustment of the back focus. However, the focus shift caused by changing between white light and infrared light is often so great that back focus adjustment does not find a common point such that a good quality image is produced. To counteract this effect, a special lens modification bends the IR light at a closer angle to that of the various visible light colours. These lenses are known as IR-corrected and should be used when using IR illumination.

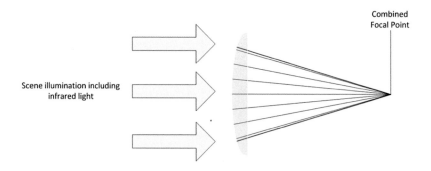

Figure 27 Light Passing Through an IR-Corrected Lens

The correct size and type of camera lens is critical to a CCTV system. It must gather the light correctly and focus it onto the chip; without this the images will be useless. Selecting the right focal length to achieve the operational requirement of the camera is also essential to a successful system design.

Housings

When positioning a CCTV camera, it is important to consider the local environmental issues that may affect the camera or its performance. In a normal office environment and assuming that there is no risk of anybody tampering with the camera, it can be located without a housing. However there are not many environments like this when CCTV is required where the equipment will remain dry, clean and safe.

Environmental housings protect the camera from weather conditions such as heat, cold, wet, wind, etc. Housings can also protect a camera from dust or a corrosive atmosphere such as chlorine gas. A camera located near the coast would need special consideration because of the corrosive nature of the salt spray in the air.

The level of protection against ingress of material into a housing is measured via the IP (Ingress Protection) rating scheme. The IP rating is normally made up from two numbers. There is a third number that rates the protection against impact but it is rarely used in relation to security systems.

The first digit in the two-digit number rates the equipment's protection against solid objects.

Digit	Ingress Protection
0	No rated protection
1	Protected against objects over 50mm
2	Protected against objects over 12mm
3	Protected against objects over 2.5mm
4	Protected against objects over 1mm
5	Protected against limited dust ingress
6	No dust ingress.

The second digit in the two-digit number rates the equipment's protection against water.

Digit	Ingress Protection
0	No rated protection
1	Protection against vertically falling drops
2	Protection against direct spray up to 15o from vertical
3	Protection against direct spray up to 60o from vertical
4	Protection against direct spray from any angle (limited ingress allowed)
5	Protection against low-pressure jet from any angle (limited ingress allowed)
6	Protection against temporary flooding
7	Protection against the effects of immersion up to 15cm
8	Protection against long periods of immersion under pressure.

Figure 28 Ingress Protection Table

An example of an IP rating would be a camera housing rated at IP65. The first digit being six indicates that the housing will totally protect against the ingress of dust and the second digit being number five indicates that it will also protect against a low-pressure jet of water fired from any direction. This housing would be suitable for external use.

Some camera housings are designed to help the CCTV system blend in with the aesthetics of a building or space. These housings are manufactured specifically to match or complement the surrounding architecture or treatment.

Whatever the purpose of the housing there are two basic types – covert and overt. Covert housings are dome assemblies that generally restrict the ability for an onlooker to see in which direction the camera is pointing hence being referred to as covert. An overt housing is an assembly that contains a conventional camera within. It is referred to as overt because an observer can clearly see in which direction the camera is pointing. Both types of housings have variable designs to protect the equipment from whichever environmental condition is prevalent.

With the environment considered, it is also necessary to select the best mounting option to achieve the operational requirement, fix the equipment to the structure and ensure that it remains maintainable.

There is a vast array of brackets available to mount cameras on buildings or over parapets but sometimes there is simply nothing to mount the camera on. In these situations, a camera column is required. Camera columns come in a range of styles from open-lattice and tubular structures to lowering-head and tilt-down types. There are many considerations in choosing the best camera column to make sure that the result is fit for purpose, safe and maintainable. These are discussed later in this section.

Environmental Housing

The enclosure that protects a camera and its associated equipment from adverse weather conditions is known as an environmental housing. These units come in a range of styles from dust protection

58

to all-weather protection and even submersible. Although the electronics of a camera can work to relatively low temperatures, many items of equipment struggle below 0°C. An environmental housing can contain a heater and thermostat to maintain the temperature within the housing between the operational tolerances of the equipment within. The housing also protects the electronics and optics from moisture. However, condensation can still be an issue if the external temperature varies considerably. It is always worthwhile putting a bag of silica gel beads in the housing to reduce the humidity as this will help with condensation problems. The heater is mounted at the front of the housing just below the vision panel which uses convection to keep the screen clear. If condensation is difficult to avoid then a fan can be installed within the housing as well to circulate the warm air.

An environmental housing protects the camera assembly from water damage by being a sealed unit. A rain lip can reduce the amount of water running across the vision panel but a wiper, and if necessary a washer, can also be fitted to the front of the housing to wipe away rain and dirt.

Rain is not the only weather condition that can be alleviated by an environmental housing. An extendable sun shield can reduce the amount of glare into the housing and camera lens. Ideally, the sun shield should be matt black on the inside to reduce reflection. For very sunny conditions, the sun shield introduces an air gap between the shield surface and the body of the camera housing. This reduces the effects of thermal gain through conduction from heat introduced by direct sunlight.

Anti-Tamper Housing

Some camera housings offer anti-tamper protection. Many cameras come pre-built with polycarbonate mini-dome housings. These units offer little protection against the weather or other elements that can affect the camera but they reduce the risk of malicious tampering and are ideal in internal situations.

Vandal-Resistant Housing

Vandal resistance is a difficult concept to quantify. A vandal without tools will struggle to damage most cameras within a housing. A vandal with tools is where the problem becomes apparent. What tools does the vandal have? A set of security screwdrivers is difficult to protect against and so is extreme force from an axe. The general guidance for vandal resistance is against blunt force impact. A good vandal-resistant housing should be able to withstand a limited hammer attack. The nature of the polycarbonate material used and the shape of the dome means that a dome camera can offer a relatively high protection against this type of attack.

Architectural Housing

Landmark buildings, corporate headquarters and any buildings where design and aesthetics are important require a camera housing that fits in with or complements its surroundings. Designers and architects want more than just technical solutions; they want the equipment to integrate with the overall design of the space. Some camera and housing manufacturers supply housings that do exactly this. Whether they are a stainless steel bubble or a burnished wood finish, these housings are designed to be used in areas where aesthetics are important as well as protection of the equipment.

Specialised Housings

There are some instances where a special environmental housing is required. Many industrial processes require electronic equipment to be intrinsically safe. A camera in a petro-chemical plant for example must have no method of ignition. In this case an intrinsically safe housing would be specified. Other scenarios may need submersible or blast-resistant cameras, anti-ligature housings for a custodial environment etc. Again, there is a range of specialist environmental housings for all of these scenarios.

Columns and Brackets

To ensure the best mounting solution for each camera, it is necessary to think about where they are to be sited. The height and location of the camera will dictate the type of column or bracket required. A camera mounted above a safe working height will need to be accessed for maintenance either by a machine that will raise the engineer or by a mechanical device that will lower the camera equipment. If the camera extends horizontally beyond the working platform then a swing-arm bracket may be required to return the camera to a safe place while an engineer is working on it. However, the two main considerations are safety for engineer access and weight. It is essential that once the correct bracket is selected to mount to the structure, in the best location and with safe access, it should not be overloaded. The combined weight of all of the equipment mounted on the bracket needs to be calculated to ensure that the bracket is strong enough. In addition to this, an overhead weight needs to be calculated to provide enough tolerance for wind load and the accumulation of snow etc.

There will be situations when a camera needs to be deployed at height and extended out from a working platform. The flat roof of a building or multi-storey car park may be the ideal mounting location for a high-level camera. These locations usually do not have structures extending up and out that are suitable for a camera to be mounted on. In these situations, a swing-arm bracket may be appropriate. A swing-arm bracket is one that fixes to the working platform and pivots horizontally away from the platform to locate the camera in free space. These brackets allow for safe maintenance as they can be retracted back to the working platform for service or repairs as necessary.

Mounting a camera on a column or bracket usually requires a separate location for the power supply and control equipment. A weather-proof box or cabinet is often provided in an accessible location for ease of maintenance. The control equipment is contained within and the control, power and signal cables are routed through the bracket or column to the camera housing. Camera columns can be supplied with integral base cabinets so that the control equipment is accessible at the base of the column. Whatever type of equipment enclosure is selected, it is important to consider the effects of water ingress and condensation. This may mean that a trace heater is installed or the cabinet is vented to allow air movement through convection. Condensation forms when water vapour in warm air meets a cold surface. As temperatures vary throughout the day, water droplets can form on the electronic equipment inside a cabinet. A low wattage anti-condensation heater will maintain a more even and warm temperature within the enclosure which will reduce the risk of condensation forming.

Illumination

Colour CCTV cameras respond to the 'visible light' spectrum, which has a wavelength ranging from about 400 to 700 nanometres (nm). Within this range of wavelengths are the separate colours of the

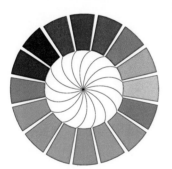

rainbow which when combined make up white light. A colour wheel can be used to demonstrate that white light is actually a combination of all of the colours of the rainbow. By spinning a disk that has a range of colours painted on it which graduate between red, yellow, blue and then back to red, you will see that they merge into a single white disk as it spins faster and faster.

Figure 29 The Content of White Light

The light in the field of view that the camera picks up can come from two sources – either direct or reflected. Direct light comes from the sun or lamps, floodlights, spotlights, street lights etc. and shines directly into the camera while reflected light is that bounced back from any surface within the scene. The reflected light is what the camera actually picks up to produce the image but the quality of the reflected light is dependent on the light source and the nature of the surface that is reflecting it. The scene illumination is reflected light that is measured in lumens per square metre, usually referred to as lux.

A CCTV camera depends on light being focused through the lens and onto the CCD chip and without sufficient illumination, the image will not be usable. Without optimum illumination, the image will be impaired. In terms of a CCTV system, light is broken down into two influences chrominance and luminance. Chrominance is the range of colours that makes up the light, and luminance is the intensity of the light. The diverse frequencies that make up light are measured by their wavelength in nanometres (nm). Depending on the make and model, CCTV cameras respond to the varying frequencies of light differently. This is known as the spectral response of the camera. Spectral response is important because if the available light is not balanced or a clean white light, a predominant frequency will tint the image towards a certain colour. For example, some artificial lights emit more yellow than blue which can give an orange glow to the light. Sometimes this glow is not noticed by the human eye but is intensified if the camera has a greater response to the yellow frequency. A white light made up from even concentrations of each separate colour will result in a clearer CCTV image with better colour rendition.

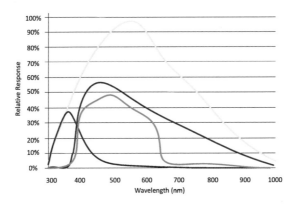

Figure 30 A Typical Spectral Response Chart

Luminance is the intensity of the light and generally the more the better, within reason. CCTV cameras have many devices to restrict the amount of light being processed so that they can optimise what they receive. The lens has an iris that shuts down, the camera speeds up the number of captures that it makes per second and the digital signal processing sorts out any residual difficulties. The problem comes when there is insufficient light and the camera has to increase its sensitivity to compensate which often introduces noise or motion blur into the picture. This noise is seen as a grainy interference in the resulting image.

A monochrome camera does not respond to colour or chrominance; it only needs brightness or luminance to display the gray scales of the scene. A monochrome camera can see beyond the visible light spectrum into the infrared (IR) spectrum which ranges from around 750 to 900 nanometres because it reacts to the brightness of the infrared light which is invisible to the naked eye. A 750 nanometre IR illuminator produces a red glow when viewed directly into the lamp whereas a 900 nanometre lamp does not emit any visible light at all.

There are many light sources available to artificially illuminate a scene but it is important to remember that the light that the camera uses does not come directly from the emitting light source; the camera receives the light that is reflected from the scene. The light falls upon the target and, depending on the make-up of the surface, only a fraction of the light is reflected towards the camera. A dark surface, such as tarmac or a building covered in dark brown cladding, will reflect less light than a plain concrete yard or a light coloured wall.

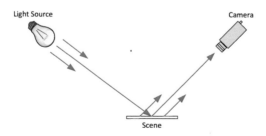

Figure 31 Light Reflectance

A common mistake made when designing a camera system is when a reading is taken to measure the amount of light hitting a scene and this figure is used to establish how sensitive the camera has to be. A more useful reading is to measure the amount of light reflected from the scene as this will be a substantially lower reading.

The following table indicates some typical reflectance values for a range of surfaces. The value is represented as a percentage of the amount of light that is reflected back from any given surface. In simple terms, this means that if a light source hits a surface at 150 lux and that surface has a reflectance of 75% then only 112.5 lux of light will be directed towards the camera.

Surface Material	Typical White Light Reflectance
Snow	90%
White Paper	75%
Clean Aluminium	75%
Clean Concrete	45%
Grass	40%
Brickwork	25%
Tarmac	5%

Figure 32 Typical Reflectance Table

Camera manufacturers use various techniques to determine the published performance of their products. The true technical specification for determining the sensitivity of a camera is the amount of light required at the CCD chip to produce a usable picture. Specifications that quote the minimum scene illumination are not much use unless you can calculate the amount of reflected light and then take into consideration the distance from the scene to the camera and the amount of light that passes through the optics. Even so, the specification that quotes the sensitivity at the CCD chip does not usually define what constitutes a usable picture so this figure is not definitive either. As a general rule, if you are designing a CCTV system that is operating at very low light levels, you should consider illumination rather than relying on camera sensitivity.

Transmission

With the camera selected and sited in the ideal location to achieve its operational requirement, it is important to consider the method of transmitting the video signal to the control and recording equipment. A CCTV signal is made up from a range of high-frequency components that are susceptible to interference from surrounding electromagnetic sources. There are various transmission methods available, each with their own advantages and disadvantages. Normally the transmission method is chosen based on 'fitness for purpose' and cost efficiency but sometimes there are other considerations to be taken into account, the primary one being distance. A conventional coaxial cable can only efficiently transmit a colour video signal over 250m whereas a twisted pair or fibre-optic transmission system can transmit the same signal over several kilometres. The selection of the most appropriate transmission system is critical to receiving quality video signals at the control equipment without over-engineering a solution.

Coaxial Cable

Coaxial cable is made up from an inner metal conductor surrounded by a tube of metal braid that forms the second conductor. A protective outer jacket surrounds the whole cable. This construction offers a limited protection against noise induced by adjacent high power cables or other sources of electromagnetic interference. The distance that a video signal can be transmitted along a coaxial cable is limited by the electrical properties of the cable construction. There is a range of coaxial cables available that has different properties depending on the distance required and the environment in which the cable is installed. Coaxial cable is the only viable transmission method that does not need additional send-and-receive equipment. The following chart gives an indication of the distance that the most common coaxial cables used in CCTV systems can send a colour signal before degradation is apparent.

Cable Type	Distance (m)
RG59	250
RG6	300
RG11	450

Figure 33 Coax Comparison Table

Twisted Pair

CCTV video signals require unbalanced line transmission systems due to their electrical characteristics. This means that coaxial cable is the natural method of transmission for CCTV. The shield of the coaxial cable is connected to electrical ground which absorbs most of the electrical interference that it encounters. However, a balanced transmission system can send the signal further than coax without picking up interference.

A balanced signal transmission system uses an unshielded twisted pair (UTP) cable. Any induced interference is picked up by both cores of the twisted pair and is effectively electronically cancelled out. To enable the video signal to be transmitted over a twisted pair cable, a balun is required. A balun is a device that allows the video signal to be transmitted by converting the electrical signal which is normally unbalanced in relation to the ground to one that is balanced and vice versa. The word balun is derived from balanced/unbalanced. The balun is a physical device that plugs onto either end of the UTP cable to make the conversion. Many cameras are supplied with an optional integral video balun.

This method of transmission has several advantages over standard coaxial transmission in that longer distances can be achieved with a better immunity to interference. The use of twisted pair cable means that multi-core cables can be used to allow multiple video signals to be transmitted along a single cable. Another use of multi-core cable is to use the additional cores to transmit the power and data for the camera. However, caution is required when considering power-over-twisted-pair cable to ensure that, firstly, the cable is rated for the electrical load and, secondly, that the resistance value of the cable does not result in a drop in voltage which starves the equipment of power.

An enhanced balanced transmission system uses powered or 'active' baluns. These units allow for greater transmission distances and signal optimisation adjustment. The following chart gives an indication of the distance over which various combinations of transmitter and receiver used for CCTV can send a colour signal before degradation is apparent.

Transmission Type	Distance (m)
Passive	225
Passive – Active	1,000
Active – Active	1,600 +

Figure 34 UPT Transmission Comparison Table

Fibre-Optic

Fibre-optic (FO) links convert electrical signals into a light source at the transmitting device, send the signal over a glass or plastic fibre and then convert the light back to electrical signals for output at the receiver. Fibre-optic transmission is immune to electromagnetic interference which makes it ideal for long-distance transmission or for installation in hostile electromagnetic environments. The reverse effect of fibre optic cables being immune to electromagnetic interference is that they do not emit any electromagnetic signal. This means that it is very difficult to intercept the video signals along the cable without breaking it and inserting a receiver. This is one of the reasons why fibre-optic cables are used in high-security installations.

In simple terms, the fibre-optic transmission system architecture consists of a transmitter and receiver. The transmitter is located at the field equipment and converts the analogue video from the camera to digital video for transmission via light signals. The receiver is located at the control equipment location where it converts the light back to a conventional electronic video signal. It is possible to send

68

multiple video signals over a single fibre by using a technology known as time division multiplexing. This allows multiple signals to be split into tiny time fragments and be transmitted effectively simultaneously. The result is multiple near-perfect images at the receiving end.

The available bandwidth on a fibre-optic cable makes it a very versatile transmission system. This means that fibre-optic transmission can also include additional channels for telemetry data, audio, Ethernet or clean contact closure among many other things.

The transmission element within the fibre-optic cable is made up from a central transparent core which carries the signal in light form and a surrounding cladding that contains it within the core. There are two main categories of fibre-optic cable – single-mode and multi-mode. Single-mode is more expensive than multi-mode but because it has a smaller core the light passes through it with fewer reflections. Each reflection introduces a very small amount of distortion which means that with single-mode cable the light can travel further without degradation.

Multi-mode fibre has a larger core that allows multiple modes of light to pass through which means that more data can be transmitted. However, because of the increased number of reflections and therefore distortions, the signal cannot travel as far as it can within a single-mode cable. The following chart gives an indication of the distance each type of fibre-optic cable used for CCTV can send a colour signal before degradation is apparent.

Transmission Type	Distance (m)
Multi-mode	3,000
Single-mode	30,000

Figure 35 Fibre-Optic Transmission Comparison Table

Data Transmission

Video is not the only information that needs transmitting within a CCTV system. Telemetry data is the signal that commands the pan, tilt, zoom and auxiliary controls of a fully-functional camera. The data contains instructions for commands such as pan left, pan right, tilt up or tilt down, wash, wipe, lights on etc. This type of data is often transmitted in a standard data format known as RS data.

RS-485 and RS-422 data can be transmitted across compatible copper cable for up to 1,200 metres or around 4,000 feet. RS-232 can only be transmitted a few metres as it has to transmit and receive a clock pulse which limits the distance that it can travel without loss. Beyond these distances, fibre-optic cable can be used or powered launch amplifiers can be installed to boost the signal over the copper cable.

It is advisable to leave the choice of a cable type for RS data transmission to the device manufacturer as losses are dependent on several electrical factors and the number of cores required may vary for the data configuration. Generally, the cable will be either a two or a four-core twisted pair type. Some manufacturers recommend an overall shield within the cable to reduce loss and interference.

The key consideration with data transmission is the distance. The following chart gives an indication of the distance that various serial data standards used for CCTV can send a signal before degradation is apparent. It is important to note that distance is heavily affected by the baud rate of the data.

Data Standard	Distance (m)
RS-232	15
RS-485	1,200
RS-422	1,500

Figure 36 Typical Transmission over Copper Cable

Internet Protocol (IP)

The advent of Ethernet with both local and wide area networks has allowed CCTV images to be sent around the globe. The image is converted to an internet protocol data stream that passes through local networks and then across the wider internet. Using IP transmission has many advantages over traditional point-to-point transmission. IP has the ability to be received at multiple locations. Dependant on the system deployed, the CCTV system could be configured to stream video at one resolution to an archiving server, while simultaneously streaming a higher resolution to an operator system. This has the advantage of saving storage space by archiving at a lower resolution while the operator receives high-quality, high-resolution images for live viewing.

IP transmission converges CCTV with information technology and all of the benefits that come with it. However, using IP transmission has some other advantages over traditional methods in that extending an existing local area network to incorporate IP CCTV may offer significant financial savings over installing new point-to-point cables. Utilising a network infrastructure may offer an element of future-proofing as this is the direction that the industry is taking, with some manufacturers abandoning their analogue product range.

Converging CCTV with information technology also allows the use of security information management software (PSIM) to analyse video content, consider information from other systems and present the operator with only relevant information to act upon.

However, when installing a new IP system there are limitations to be considered with Ethernet cabling in that distances are limited to 90 metres or 100 feet when using copper cable. This means that mid-span switches may be necessary or media converters used to convert the data to fibre-optic transmission. However, these switches may contain power over Ethernet (PoE) technology that can be used to power the camera equipment. There are problems with the amount of power that some CCTV equipment needs and the capabilities of power over Ethernet. The power is limited by the resistance on the Cat5 or Cat6 cable and some CCTV equipment needs more power than the system can provide unless a local power supply is used. An indoor static camera is usually fine at 90m on PoE but fully-functional cameras and external equipment that needs a heater are likely to have power problems unless the correct voltage drop calculations are made.

Wireless Video and Data

If it is not practical to install cables for a CCTV system then there is the alternative transmission method of wireless CCTV. Wireless transmission makes it possible to site a camera almost anywhere, especially if the camera has its own onboard power supply such as a battery or solar panel. Wireless transmission makes temporary, rapid deployment cameras a viable option for many applications. These cameras are often installed in town or city centres where power is available on street lighting columns. These columns often offer a good vantage point to monitor whatever the target scene may be, whether it is a busy intersection, a meeting point for gangs or an area of known criminal activity. A general point to note is that light columns are not designed to have cameras mounted on them. Camera columns are sturdier to reduce movement caused by the wind, so a camera mounted on a light column may move around a bit on a windy day.

There are generally three types of wireless radio technologies used for CCTV deployment: analogue, digital and IP. The term 'open space' is used in relation to range because all wireless transmission systems are limited by the built environment around them. Radio signals are reflected and absorbed at different rates by different material so that no one location can be said to be the same as another in terms of range. If you consider that radio frequencies act in a similar way to light frequencies then you will see that some materials such as polished metal reflect a lot of light leaving a shadow behind them and some allow light to travel through, such as glass. Although radio waves react with each material in a slightly different way to light, the principle is the same: reflections and shadows.

Analogue transmission has a limited range in open space; typically less than 100m whereas digital wireless transmission in general has a transmission range of just over 100m in open space. Digital transmission is also less susceptible to interference than analogue.

> *Wireless transmission is restricted by buildings and the landscape. Care must be taken to ensure that the signals are strong enough or there are enough transmitters and receivers to complete the link.*

A more developed wireless transmission technology would be a wireless IP network topology allowing the transmission of internet protocol CCTV images and data over a mesh of transmitters so giving the system a layer of resilience and range in its configuration. A camera or any other IP device can be connected at any node on the mesh.

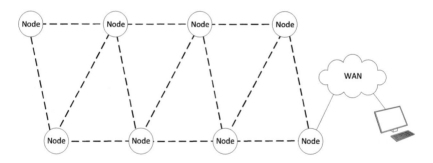

Figure 37 Wireless IP Mesh Network

If a less sophisticated single wireless link is required for a single or multiplexed video signal then a point-to-point system can be deployed which uses either microwave (MW) or infrared (IR) beams to carry the video signal. The signal is converted to either microwave or infrared and sent via a transmitter to an aligned receiver. Both systems need line of sight but microwave can send a signal much further than infrared. Infrared is also more likely to be affected by inclement weather.

Whichever wireless transmission system is used, it is important to note that alignment and the rigidity of the installed equipment are essential to the correct and continued operation of the link.

Transient Suppression

All modern societies rely heavily upon electronics for every aspect of life; from health and commerce to entertainment and security. The basic fact about electronics is that it uses wires or cables to transmit power and signals. Let's put wireless to one side for now because there is not yet a viable wireless power transmission technology which means that even wireless systems rely on connection cables at some level.

This fundamental reliance upon metal conductors means that one rule of physics is unavoidable. Michael Faraday first published his discovery of electromagnetic induction in 1831. He explained that electromagnetic fields can induce electricity into an adjacent metal conductor without physical connection. Therefore, an intense burst of power near a cable can induce a damaging spike of electricity into the adjacent cable without being in physical contact with it. This spike is likely to damage or disable the electrical systems that the cable serves.

Lightning is a big culprit for causing these dangerous spikes given its strength and the amount of cable lying across the planet but lightning is not the only source of damaging spikes. Spikes are more likely to be caused in a CCTV system by heavy machinery switching on. Motors and appliances such as air conditioning can also cause damaging transient voltage spikes when they start up.

Another term used in connection with these spikes is overvoltage. The term transient overvoltage literally means a momentary electrical spike. These spikes can rapidly overheat components in the electrical system or breakdown the insulation of components that contain the signals. Either way, system damage can be catastrophic.

You may have designed the best CCTV system in the world but it will be at risk of problems or complete failure if you don't consider transient protection. The difficulty for the system designer is to keep the amount of protection proportional to the risk of induced overvoltage. You may think that a domestic property in a low lightning area would need far less protection than an industrial process plant in a high-risk lightning area. This assumption is probably correct but the risk assessment for how much protection is required needs to consider the potential impact should a system fail as well as the hazards that may cause the voltage spike.

Let's consider the domestic property again. The property does not have any heavy machinery turning on and off but it does have air conditioning which is quite old. It also has domestic appliances such as refrigerators etc. The wiring in the property is also old and is bunched up as it runs around the house. It is a large house that belongs to a very wealthy person who doesn't trust the banking system so he keeps a large quantity of money on the premises in a safe. Although the property is in a low lightning risk area, it is not unheard of for lightning to strike the ground occasionally. This person is often away on business and leaves the house empty for days at a time, relying on the security system to alert him and the authorities if anything unusual occurs. The risk of transient overvoltage affecting this security system is quite low but the potential for loss is quite high. So the question is: does this domestic property in a low risk area need transient suppression to protect the security system?

Any element of a system that is externally mounted is at a potential risk from a lightning strike. Building-mounted cameras are usually protected by the building's own structural lightning protection system but equipment that is raised above the roof or column mounted away from the building is at a higher risk of a direct hit. If this happens, you can probably say goodbye to the equipment that took the full force of the strike but the transients can travel along the cable and severely damage anything else connected to the system.

Transient overvoltage can also be induced from one cable into another that is running in parallel to it. This means that if a radio antenna, for example, is hit and the CCTV cables run in parallel to the radio cables, then the CCTV system can suffer damage as well. The practical solution to avoiding this problem is to ensure that all cables that enter a building have transient suppression devices fitted at the point of entry to the building. Whether the system is a radio antenna, television, telephone, mains power or anything that feeds the property with metallic cables, they should be suppressed. This is relatively easy to achieve on a new building but not so easy on an old one. In which case, the CCTV system needs to have suppression fitted at the point of entry to the building to ensure that no other systems are damaged but also at the equipment racks in case damaging transients are induced from another, older system.

Transient protection devices connect to every core of a metallic cable (as opposed to fibre-optic cable which is immune to transient overvoltages) and remain 'transparent' to the system. It is important that every core and cable shield or screen is protected because it only takes one link to pass the damaging spike. The device passes the power or data signal through without any interruption but as soon as a voltage is detected that is higher than the rating of the device, it is directed safely to earth.

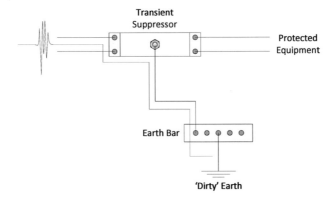

Figure 38 Transient Suppression

> *A point to note when designing a transient protection system is where the 'dirty' earth cable runs. If the earth cable runs parallel with CCTV cables, the transients could be re-introduced into the protected side of the system.*

CCTV Control Equipment

The field equipment of a CCTV system and its location is critical to achieve the operational requirements of the overall system. However, apart from the field equipment, a complete operational requirements document will also detail the human interface, evidential archive and associated procedures. For this, the control equipment must be selected to be proportional and appropriate to ensure that the collated information and the way it is presented to an operator is in the most efficient form.

The control equipment in a CCTV system can be broken down into three sub-categories: display equipment, video switching and archive. Each sub-category can be broken down further as manufacturers have all developed their own spin on functionality but for the purposes of this discussion, we shall keep to the general functionality of each sub-category.

Video Display

Small-scale systems rely upon one or two video monitors to display the CCTV images. CRT or old-style glass tube monitors are rare in modern systems having been replaced by flat screen technology. Thin film transistor liquid crystal display (TFT LCD) technology has enabled CCTV monitors to become flatter and more energy-efficient. However, their mass production has been driven by the television and computer monitor market which has resulted in many of the screens being manufactured to 16:9 aspect ratio. The aspect ratio is the shape or dimensions of the video image and conventional CCTV cameras have an aspect ratio of 4:3. This means that for every four units of measurement horizontally there are three of the same unit vertically. For example, if the image is 48 centimetres wide it must be 36 centimetres high. By contrast, a 16:9 aspect ratio is wide-screen format where if the image is 48 centimetres wide it must be 27 centimetres high. If a conventional CCTV image is displayed on a 16:9 monitor there will be horizontal stretch distortion in the displayed image. Alternatively, there will be a solid black vertical bar either side of the image. Care must be taken when selecting the display monitor to avoid distortion. Many IP cameras produce a wide-screen image so a wide-screen monitor is therefore required.

4:3 Image on a 16:9 Screen   4:3 Image on a 4:3 Screen

16:9 Image on a 16:9 Screen   16:9 Image on a 4:3 Screen

Figure 39 Aspect Ratio

Small-scale IP CCTV systems may not use dedicated monitors to display the individual images. A software application will display single or multiple images within a window on a PC monitor, allowing other information and control functionality to be displayed on the same screen.

CCTV systems that feed into a control room may be displayed on large screens or a video wall. Video walls can be made up from a range of technologies including LCD and rear-projection cubes. LCD screens with LED backlights and narrow bezel edges can be tiled to form a much larger screen. For larger control rooms, rear projection cubes are available. These cubes stack with relatively small seams between each one so forming a potentially very large video wall.

Whichever display technology is chosen, it is essential to get the right video wall controller to allow the images to be spread across the multiple screens that form the wall. The video wall controller brings additional functionality to the wall by allowing different types of video and data to be displayed as well as allowing it to be displayed on different sections of the wall dependant on the operational requirements at the time. For example, a site plan graphic can be shrunk and positioned to one side during an alarm event to allow the alarm verification CCTV images to be displayed centre-screen. The graphic will return to centre on alarm reset.

Video wall layouts and management offer almost limitless scenarios for control room applications but a point to note is that of resilience. If the entire control room relies upon a video wall that is controlled by a single video server then a single point of failure has been introduced into the system. If this server fails, the whole control room goes blind.

Digital Video Recording

The technology involved in recording video data is developing at a rapid pace due to consumer demand for more and more storage space. Terabyte (TB) archive recorders are now commonplace. With this amount of storage space, it is possible to archive high-quality, high-frame-rate images for a considerable amount of time.

Before the advent of mass storage, the emphasis on digital recording was to compress the image as much as possible to reduce the file size and only record a few images per second. When a video signal is digitised, it has a size that is measured in bytes of data that make up a single image. The image is the digital equivalent of the analogue 'frame'. The amount of images per second recorded affects the smoothness of the playback. Typically, in the UK 25 images per second is considered a 'live' image and 30 images per second in the US. These figures are based on analogue technology which uses the frequency of the mains power to synchronise the frame. With each frame being made up from two fields, the UK 50 hertz (cycles per second) power supply made 25 frames per second the standard 'live' video. With the US mains power frequency being 60 hertz, 30 frames per second became the norm. The human eye starts to see smooth images from about 12 images per second and upwards but 25 images per second has remained the standard.

Compression of the signal, in its simplest form, removes bits of data from the image file hence reducing its size and quality. So a trade-off is needed between quality and the amount of time a video stream is archived for. Video compression techniques have improved rapidly over recent years partly due to the need to store high-quality images and partly due to the need to transmit them via cable and satellite for domestic television purposes. The result today is that good quality compression and mass storage mean that multiple camera systems can archive video for many months.

Video recording in a CCTV system can be achieved with a standard digital video recorder (DVR) or via a Networked Video Recorder (NVR).

A DVR compresses analogue video signals that are connected directly to the recorder. The recorder digitises the signals and stores them on the hard disks within the recorder. By contrast, an NVR stores IP video signals directly from a network to a networked storage device. Both systems are scalable but the NVR offers more flexibility in terms of the size and the fact that the location of the storage media can be anywhere on the network. Many systems offer a hybrid of DVR and NVR in that the DVR can also accept networked video.

In many circumstances, the archived video is of great importance and value such that some systems employ a resilient configuration of hard disks known as RAID (Redundant Array of Independent Disks). Disk failure is relatively common; a RAID array combines multiple drives and spreads the data across the array. There are several ways that data is distributed within a RAID system and each way is referred to as a 'level'. Generally, the higher the RAID level, the better the system resilience to the effects of a disk failure. The RAID system partitions each drive unit and then stripes the data across several partitions and across several disks. Higher levels of RAID then employ a technique known as parity which checks whether the data has been lost. There were five original RAID levels but manufacturers have created variations of these as well as nested levels to provide even more resilient solutions.

RAID 0 has striping but no parity and no built-in redundancy.

RAID 1 duplicates the data across two or more disks. RAID 1 has no striping or parity. This technique is sometimes called mirroring or mirrored disks.

RAID 2 uses striping across the array of disks with some of the disks storing error-checking and correction information.

RAID 3 uses striping across the array of disks with one disk dedicated to storing error-checking and correction information.

RAID 4 uses large stripes which mean that the system can overlap read operations. It dedicates one disk to storing error checking and correction information.

RAID 5 uses large stripes but also distributes the error-checking and correction information. The parity data can reconstruct lost data.

RAID 6 is the same as five but with an additional parity method to increase the fault tolerance.

Having considered resilience, there are further options for storing the video archive. Where the recording is located and how it is managed are both important subjects. Many countries have legislation protecting electronic data than can identify an individual. The data cannot be stored for longer than is necessary, it must be relevant, it must not infringe privacy legislation etc. One of the basic principles of legislation is the protection of the data which means that the hard disks must be in a secure environment and access to the system needs to be controlled by a password or similar so that only authorised people can view the data.

Traditionally, digital video recording has been local to the CCTV system. With the advent of IP systems and Network Video Recorders, some CCTV systems have converged with IT systems and utilise a centralised Storage Area Network (SAN). A SAN is a sub-network specifically designed to share storage. The network architecture allows the various storages devices to be accessed by the servers on the larger network beyond the SAN.

Some systems utilise iSCSI technology (Internet Small Computer System Interface) to manage mass storage in a similar manner to a SAN. SCSI is the most common method of communicating with a RAID array. iSCSI is the same technology but with the ability to communicate via a network instead of a 'hard' connection between devices. The advantage of this is that the system can have its own centralised RAID storage array and the IP cameras can communicate directly to it without the need for a video server. The removal of the server means that video streaming processor limitations are reduced and system reliability is increased.

Even with the rapid development of digital recording technology, it is still important to consider the file size of the image based on the resolution, the quality, how many images per second are required and how much change or movement will be in the image. This information is used to calculate the storage size so that one can be certain that if the operational requirement states that 30 days of archive is required for example, then that is what will be achieved.

The calculation for the size of the storage medium for a single camera is the average file size multiplied by the number of images per second, multiplied by 60 to get the storage size per minute. This number is then multiplied by 60 again to get the storage size per hour and again by 24 to get the size per day and so on. The variable is the amount of activity in the field of view because this dramatically affects the image file size. A camera located in a busy train station will have a higher average file size than one located in a locked store room. A point to note is that extraneous movement caused by noise within the video signal can increase the average file size. Noise is usually introduced in one of two ways; either electromagnetic interference or by the AGC within the camera trying to get a usable picture in low-light conditions. The example above which suggest that the camera in a locked store room will have a lower average file size than one on a busy train platform is only true if the lights stay on or the camera is commissioned in such a way that noise is not introduced when the lights go off. Another often overlooked condition that can increase file size is varying light conditions or an auto-iris lens that is hunting for the optimum light level.

Many systems allow audio recording and some allow stereo audio recording. However, a point to note is that not all systems lip synchronise the audio to the video. It is thought that at least 12 images per second are required to get lip-sync but there is another factor to consider. The recording technology must get the audio time synchronised to the video within 50 milliseconds for it to be considered as lip-synchronised.

Whether DVR or NVR, local or mass storage, the purpose of digital video recording is to archive video. The system operational requirement will determine what the archived video is for but it is good practice to assume that the video recording could end up as evidence in a legal case. In which case, it would come under intense scrutiny so it is essential that the recording is robust. Time and date is obviously very important when it comes to evidential recording. Multiple DVRs should be time-synchronised to ensure that recordings from different devices on the same system display exactly the same time if two cameras are played back simultaneously. Time synchronisation should ideally come from a GPS clock or network time server so that it is always correct.

As a minimum to stand up as evidence, a video recording must be able to demonstrate an audit trail from the moment it was recorded to the point that it was submitted as evidence. The integrity of the video must be demonstrated to prove that it has not been tampered with. Digital watermarking and fingerprinting techniques can be employed to detect any tampering with an image.

The recorded video evidence should be encrypted in such a way that it is very difficult to reconstruct it without the reverse algorithm. The data should be stored in a physically secure place but also be secure against unauthorised electronic access. As part of the audit trail, the system should log who has accessed the video data, when, and what they did with it. This is often overlooked on small-scale IP systems where network access is not always strictly controlled.

It must be possible to export the video data to Write-Once-Read-Many (WORM) media such as CD or DVD. The exported recording should also contain a copy of the playback software, including the reverse algorithm for the encryption. If the system can export the DVR event log and audit trail, it will help with establishing the integrity of the evidence.

Quad Split and Multiplexers

An IP CCTV system or one that converts analogue cameras to IP video can present multiple images on one screen in a split-screen or picture-in-picture arrangement. However, in a smaller analogue system without an IP video server, to present multiple images on a screen or to record multiple images onto a single channel of recording, a quad split or multiplexer can be used.

A quad split will present or record up to four images on a screen simultaneously. It splits the screen into four segments and presents a video channel per segment. A recording from a quad split unit will always play back in the same quad format.

A multiplexer typically allows up to 16 images to be displayed on a single screen simultaneously. However, the screen needs to be quite large to make sensible use of a 16-way split image. Most multiplexers also allow for varying patterns of display such as a large image in the middle surrounded by smaller ones or picture-in-picture where two images are displayed with one small one on top of a larger one. The difference between a multiplexer and a quad split is that when you play back a multiplexed recording you can select any camera in full screen or as part of a montage.

In record mode, a multiplexer sequences the full-screen images very quickly and records all of them on a single channel. Given a system that normally records at 30 images per second with 15 cameras connected, it would record two images of any given camera per second. This means that in playback mode you will only see two images per second for that camera and this presents a time-lapse effect to the viewer. Although the video plays back in real-time, any movement will appear jerky or stop-start. The same system with only three cameras connected will record ten images per second per camera which will provide a much smoother playback.

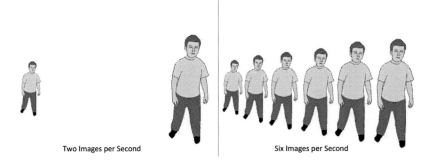

Two Images per Second   Six Images per Second

Figure 40 Multiplex Recording

To try and alleviate this reduced image rate playback, some multiplexers contain motion detection which samples more images from cameras with activity in the field of view at the cost of images from those that have no activity. For example, our system with 15 cameras connected could be programmed to record a single camera with activity at 16 images per second while all of the others record at one image per second. In reality, the record rate would be spread over several cameras with activity and each camera record rate would go up and down to suit.

Video Switching Matrix

At the heart of a larger CCTV system sits a device that manages which camera displays on which monitor. Whether IP or analogue, a fundamental component of the system is a video switching matrix. In an IP system the matrix is a virtual one because outside of the server there are no physical components that route video. In an analogue system the matrix is an electronic device that accepts a single live video feed from every camera on the system and connects it to every display device on the system.

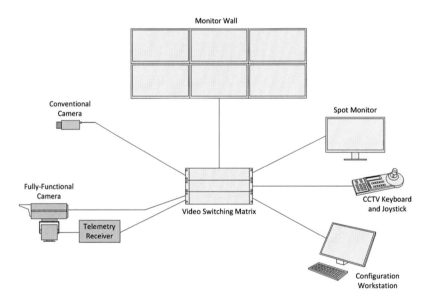

Figure 41 Video-Switching Matrix

A video switching matrix has a range of functionality that can be programmed to suit the operational requirements of the system. Manual switching of cameras allows an operator to select any camera to any monitor. If a fully-functional camera is selected, the telemetry control function for that unit's telemetry receiver board is automatically switched to the joystick so that the operator can pan, tilt and zoom the camera that is on screen.

Cameras can be switched to monitors in pre-programmed ways. A simple sequence can be programmed so that a pre-defined range of cameras can switch one after another on screen. Several of these sequences can be set up across several monitors. It can display a pre-defined set of cameras on a set pattern of monitors at a single press of a button. A guard tour can be programmed so that a fully-functional camera waiting in a 'home' position can be deployed to a pre-set field of view, wait for a period of time and then deploy to the next pre-set position, wait and then move on again. This guard tour can be used by an operator to carry out a routine inspection of the area that they are responsible for without leaving the control room.

All of the switching capabilities of a matrix can be automated with alarm inputs. In an analogue CCTV system, an alarm input is usually a clean contact that when opened or closed – dependant on the programming – triggers the matrix to react. The term 'clean contact' is used in electronics to describe a switch that opens and closes to break or complete a circuit. It is referred to as 'clean' because it does not carry any power or electronic signals.

In an IP system, there is no physical alarm input at the virtual matrix, simply a command from software or from another networked device. In the event of an alarm input changing state or the virtual matrix receiving a command, the matrix can either bring a single camera to a single monitor, a range of cameras to a range of monitors (a salvo) or any of the other programmable display options can be deployed.

Large analogue video switching matrices can be deployed so that two control rooms can see each other's cameras. Using trunk video links connected from the monitor outputs of one matrix and via an IP transmission system (codecs) to the camera inputs of another, each control room can select and control cameras from the other's system. This technique is widely used for town centre systems where control rooms take on other areas or adjacent towns. It is also used to consolidate control rooms so that money can be saved by having one large room rather than several smaller ones.

Another application of this matrix configuration is that of disaster recovery should one area need to be evacuated. A building in the financial centre of a city is often high profile and maybe subjected to bomb or terrorist threats. Having control of the security system from a remote location means that the building can be safely evacuated and remain under surveillance.

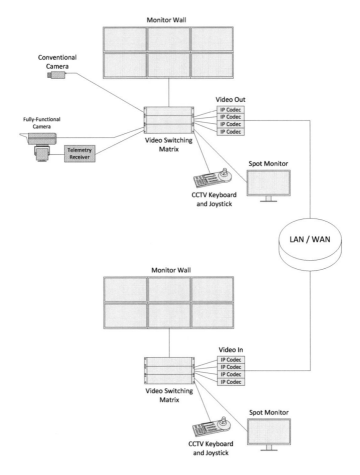

Figure 42 Video Trunks

Video Codecs

In some instances there may be a need to connect analogue cameras to an IP network. This may be for transmission, recording or for processing the signal via a virtual matrix. The method of connecting an analogue camera signal to an IP network is via a video codec (Compressor/DECompressor). A codec may be part of a digital video recorder where an analogue signal is connected to a DVR and it can then be accessed via a local area network. However, a full codec can be obtained which transmits video, audio and telemetry data in its own right via the network. These devices are manufactured in single and multi-channel variants but all allow the analogue camera to be transmitted and controlled via the local or wide area network. When the signal is on the network, it can be processed and recorded in the same way as an IP camera.

Although in this context, the term 'codec' is employed to describe a 'black box' that allows the connectivity of an analogue video source to a network, the term also applies to the sub-circuitry within a device that performs the same function. In an IP camera and many standalone devices, a good codec will have the ability to stream multiple channels of data (video streams) using different compression techniques and at different sizes. This functionality provides flexibility to adapt to the available bandwidth within a network. For example, it may be desirable to have a high-quality, bandwidth-hungry image for the local virtual matrix functionality and a lower bandwidth stream for offsite transmission and recording.

Setting the Field of View

The operational requirements document will detail what the necessary field of view is to be. To ensure ease of use, it is recommended that a camera has no more than two target objectives. The location of the camera needs to be decided upon based on achieving the desired field of view, being in a location that is safe to install and maintain and being in a location that will not pick up any damaging conditions. Electromagnetic interference near the camera or cables may introduce distortion in the image. Vibration will cause a problem and high-contrast lighting either before or behind the target will also reduce the effectiveness of the camera.

If the camera is mounted too high, the angle at which it views down will be too steep to effectively view the target. A camera mounted on the same plane as the target will provide the best field of view but this is not usually practical as it can be easily obscured or tampered with. Raising the camera up and viewing down at an angle of approximately 30^{0} often offers a good compromise.

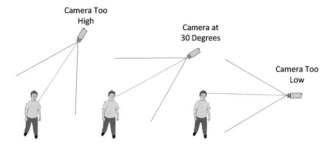

Figure 43 Camera Location and Angle of View

A telephoto lens will allow the camera to be mounted a long way from the target but the further away the camera is, the greater the chance of a lower quality image. The more a camera is zoomed in, the greater the impact of any vibration in the camera. A very small amount of movement at the camera will be amplified by the zoom of the lens, resulting in noticeable movement at the target. In addition, the greater the distance between the camera and target, the more chance you have of getting obstructions in the view. Externally these will include rain, snow, fog and heat haze which will significantly reduce the effectiveness of the camera. Consideration also needs to be given to vegetation and the effects that it will have on the field of view as it grows or as it changes with the seasons.

Avoid a location that would mean the camera has to look directly into a light source such as a street lamp or the sun. Externally, looking to the north is always preferable because any other direction is likely to be affected by the sun. East and west facing positions during the winter when the sun can be low on the horizon can be particularly bad. Also, try to avoid viewing unnecessary reflective surfaces that will interfere with the image quality as the light changes.

Although a good quality camera – especially one with wide dynamic processing features – will cope with adverse lighting conditions, it is advisable to eliminate the problems at source rather than rely on technology. With the camera located in the best possible place, you can then adjust the settings of the camera and lens to optimise the picture quality.

Detection within a CCTV System

Many CCTV systems do not have a dedicated operator and if they do, the operator usually has multiple cameras to view. Using detection technology to alert the operator to an event will enhance the effectiveness of the system. The alarm trigger can bring the relevant camera to screen, set off a sounder to alert the operator and increase the record rate and image quality.

Detection technology can also allow a system to be remotely monitored by a centralised ARC (Alarm Receiving Centre). These facilities provide a service to their customers by reacting to the alarm events, investigating them via remote access to the CCTV system and responding appropriately which may be sending a person to site or using an audio challenge system.

External Detection

There are many forms of detection technologies that will produce a contact closure to input into a CCTV system to indicate that an event has occurred. A reliable detection system will require a detailed level of design to ensure that nuisance alarms are minimised and every true event is captured. Nuisance alarms are those generated by true activity but not the activity that is sought after. Nuisance alarms are often caused by bad placement of the detector where it can see

91

moving objects such as cars or people in the distance, or foliage that moves in the wind. Nuisance alarms differ from false alarms because they are legitimate activations; false alarms are primarily due to equipment failure or poor detector design.

With nuisance alarms in mind, the detection system should take into consideration the local environment and the amount of activity within it. This may change dependant on the time of day or year. The layout of the site needs to be considered and how the site will continue to operate with detection in place.

The fundamental rule when designing a CCTV detection system is that all detectors or detection zones should be within the field of view of the camera. Without this rule an operator will get an alert with no video verification and soon put it down as a nuisance alarm. Human nature will dictate that eventually the operator will either lower the priority of that alarm or even worse, ignore it.

It is common practice, and an error, to use multiple passive infrared detectors located immediately below a fully-functional camera. The concept is that the camera will pan and zoom to each area of detection when it is activated. This configuration works if you only think about it in the horizontal plane but if you consider that a PIR detector has many fingers of detection vertically as well as horizontally, then you will see that there is a fundamental problem with mounting PIR detectors immediately below a PTZ camera.

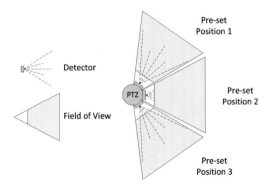

Figure 44 PIR Detection with a PTZ Camera

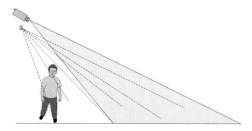

Figure 45 Blind Area below a PTZ Camera

PIR detectors reach down as well as out with their detection field, which means that it is possible to trigger the device by walking immediately underneath it. For the camera to see this area it would need to widen its zoom lens and tilt down. Equally, for the camera to see an activation at the far end of the detection field it would need to tilt up and zoom in. This means that to cover an entire PIR detection field, the PTZ camera would need multiple pre-set positions. The problem is that a PIR detector cannot discriminate between which parts of its detection field have been activated and can only give out a single contact closure. The PIR detection field should be located within the field of view of the camera so that whichever part of it is activated, the camera will see the event and provide video verification to the operator.

Detectors should be sited and limited so that they do not detect beyond the boundary of the required detection area. Consideration needs to be given to the type of activity being detected and the speed of the fully-functional camera. For example if the system is to detect a person walking across a small gap between two buildings and the camera rotates at 40° per second, it could take as long as 4½ seconds for the camera to pan around to the target. During this interval the person has crossed the gap and disappeared from view. Again, the operator will soon put these events down to nuisance alarms and start to ignore them.

93

Video Content Analysis

By its very nature, video content analysis or video analytics can only detect in the field of view of the camera. The system uses the video image to select and detect activity (change in the content of the video stream) and to provide video verification of the event.

The system processes the video stream with various algorithms to identify a predetermined activity. There are many algorithms that have been produced and they tend to fall into certain categories such as tracking, classification or behavioural.

A global algorithm is the most basic in that it is only looking for simple changes in the field of view. This form of analysis is ideal for increasing record rates when there is activity in the scene or for alerting on an event in an area that should be sterile. A basic tracking algorithm will track an object and be able to determine relative direction and speed within the scene. It is not possible for this algorithm to determine the true speed of an object because it cannot calculate the actual size of the target or where it sits within the depth of field. However, it can be used to initiate an alert if a fast-moving object crosses a predetermined area in any given direction.

A higher level of the tracking algorithm can estimate true size and speed by knowing set dimensions within the field of view that are programmed into the system during commissioning. You can programme the system to tell it that one part of the field of view is a known distance, let's say one metre long. This is done by drawing a line on the image that equates to this measurement. You then draw another line that equates to one metre but this time further away in the field of view. Tell the system how many metres these two points are apart within the depth of field and you have provided the software with depth perception. The system can then approximate size/distance and therefore speed. These algorithms are suited to external situations where the depth of field is usually far greater than that of an internal scene.

Classification algorithms identify the difference between different objects of interest. These algorithms can identify with a good level of accuracy whether an object is a person, a vehicle or something else. Once identified, the object can then be subjected to other rules such as trip wires, direction, loitering, appearing, disappearing etc. For example, this has the advantage of letting vehicles pass but not people. Imagine a CCTV system deployed on a railway track to monitor for cable theft. The system would ignore trains because they are large and fast-moving but as soon as a person entered the field of view it would recognise the difference. It may alarm at this point or the system may be programmed to only alarm if the person crosses a virtual trip wire.

Behavioural algorithms monitor the scene over a long period to establish what content and activity is normal and then alert to an operator when something different occurs. As a concept, this sounds relatively simple. A camera looking at an empty room would 'know' that empty is normal but when an object appears in the room it will alert to the operators. The operators have an option to tell the system that this object is also normal, such as a new painting on the wall. When something else changes in the room, the system will alert that event to the operators. This process effectively 'teaches' the system how to behave. The difficulty comes when dealing with a more complicated scene such as an external view. The field of view may contain foliage, traffic, shadows, sky etc. all of which change constantly. A behavioural algorithm will 'learn' normal activity over a long period of time and during commissioning will ask a stream of questions relating to what is normal activity and what is not. After a typical period of about two weeks, the system should be able to monitor an active scene and ignore the foliage, shadows and normal scene activity but still alert if something unusual happens. For example, the system is viewing a road to a private residential area. The scene is loaded with foliage, people and cars moving in various directions during the day but as soon as a large vehicle enters such as a lorry, the security office is notified. The chances are that this is a legitimate delivery but it may be considered worth highlighting the event to the operators to monitor. If a large vehicle enters in the middle of the night, the system may alert the event as a higher priority as this is not likely to be a routine delivery. All of the time, the behavioural algorithm will ignore 'normal' activity.

Video analytics are predominantly used to either optimise storage requirements or detect interesting activity and alert it to an operator. To optimise storage requirements a simple algorithm is used to detect activity or the lack of it and increase or decrease the record rate accordingly. This form of motion detection can reduce the amount of required storage space by up to 80% on an average system compared to one that is continuously recording.

Using video content analysis to identify significant activity allows the system to watch the cameras 24/7 and only alert the operator when an unusual event occurs. The following list is not exhaustive but provides an indication of the various applications available.

- Replacing traditional sensors
    o Motion detection
    o Intrusion detection
    o Perimeter detection

- System monitoring
    o Black frame detection
    o Blur detection
    o Camera displacement
    o Covered lens detection

- Specific content analysis
    o Object appearing
    o Object disappearing
    o Object loitering
    o Crossing a trip wire
    o Direction sensing
    o Smoke & fire detection
    o Detection of drowning
    o Counting and statistics

- Crowd analysis
    o Crowd density
    o Crowd flow.

Facial Recognition

Facial recognition systems use an electronically-gathered visual image of a person's face to locate distinctive and measurable biometric identifiers in order to positively identify him or her based on a template match. Typical identifiers would be the distance between eyes, width of the nose, depth of eye sockets, shape of cheekbones, length of jaw etc. There are approximately 80 nodal points on a human face that can be used to predict the identity of an individual. The advent of 3D imaging systems allows for sub-millimetre measurements of the face which is why some manufactures claim that up to 12,000 individual measurements are taken to identify a person.

A facial recognition system takes all of these measured biometric identifiers and matches them against known templates stored within the system database to identify an individual within the field of view of the camera. Although there are many advantages to facial recognition compared to other biometric systems – such as it being non-invasive by simply reading the presence of a face within a field of view of a camera – there are many technical difficulties that need to be overcome for the system to be fully successful.

The system uses the field of view from a CCTV camera to firstly identify if it is seeing a human face. Discriminating between a face and the rest of the shapes that the camera is seeing as ingredients is in itself a challenge. To help the technology make this decision it is important to ensure that the field of view is as narrow and uncluttered as possible. The lighting needs to be optimised and the camera angles need to be just right for the location. But even with this all in place the subject is moving and may not be looking in the right direction or the subject may be non-cooperative and wearing a hat and glasses or a hood as a disguise.

Audio Content Analysis

Audio analytics for detection purposes within an electronic security system have been around for some time in the form of acoustic break-glass detectors that detect the unique frequencies of breaking glass and close a contact to report the event, usually within an intruder detection system. Another form of audio analytics that has been around for a while is that used within microphonic detection systems. A very sensitive microphonic cable fixed to a fence or wall will pick up vibration within the structure, analyse the signal against known parameters and alert on an attempted breach. Gunshot detection systems identify the unique frequencies of a gun being fired and using a system of triangulation, can pin-point the source of the sound. However, more recently with the advent of IP CCTV and integrated security systems, a more advanced form of audio analytics is emerging. Complex analysis of sound detected at a scene can isolate specific acoustic patterns and determine with accuracy if the sound warrants a response from the security system.

An audio analysis system can filter the background noise and determine a range of sound such as gunshots, vehicle presence and aerosol spray cans being used. It also detects verbal aggression and stressed voices. The vocal stress and aggression detection allows the security system to pre-empt a situation by alerting an operator to the event prior to it getting out of control. For example, such a system being deployed on the wing of a correctional facility would alert officers to aggression and potentially give them time to intervene before a fight breaks out. The same technology can reduce crime in hospitals and building receptions for example.

Larger and external areas can be monitored to give an advance warning of potential problems. Gunshot detection, breaking glass and car alarm activation can be isolated and alert a control room of abnormal activity in the neighbourhood. Yet audio analytics are not always an appropriate form of detection. Some audio scenes are simply too complicated for analysis at present but for those that can be reliably analysed, the technology is another very useful tool in an integrated CCTV system.

Having integrated technology that can switch on a camera to provide video verification of an event is essential for a remotely managed system, but if audio analysis is being used, careful consideration needs to be given to the detection range of the microphones. If the system detects audio activity outside of the field of view of a camera, it may be at risk of alerting an operator who cannot see the event and will have no way of verifying what is happening. This could lead to personnel being dispatched unnecessarily, or even worse, the operator not reacting. In extreme cases the operator may ignore the alert altogether.

As with all elements of an integrated security system, this technology needs to be suited to the location of detection and needs to interact with the wider system in a meaningful way to present an operator with relevant information to empower them to make the right decision.

Human Behaviour Analysis

The modelling of human behaviour enables an electronic security system to detect and predict potential activity of interest before it has occurred. For example, the video content analysis identifies a person's direction of sight whether it is straight forward, at an object, at an individual or looking around. In a simple form, the direction of sight can be compared with the body posture to predict behaviour. Add to this whether the target is walking, standing, moving randomly, running, moving slowly etc. and some complex predications can be made such as automatic fight detection.

In the real world and outside of the laboratory, human behaviour analysis is a very complex set of algorithms which have to discount all of the irrelevant information before they can attend to the target behaviour. The system can 'learn' what is normal in a scene or employ techniques known as background and foreground subtraction. One particular problem for scene analysis when it comes to human behaviour is that of shadows. With the use of shadow-detecting algorithms and colour analysis, it is possible to remove shadows so that the target for behavioural analysis is isolated from the background.

With the target isolated it is then possible to scan the scene for interesting behaviour patterns. A disorderly motion pattern may provide an early detection of a fight that is about to break out. Behavioural analysis can provide a high level of certainty when predicting a range of behaviours from violent crime to illegal ticket selling. A busy tube station, for example, is very difficult to monitor. The power to predict miscreant activity by detecting people loitering or tracking up and down the platform is the strength of behavioural analytics. One system claims that it can detect if a person is contemplating suicide by jumping in front of a train. Analysis of past events highlights that a specific set of behaviours is displayed by a person prior to the attempted act.

A further difficulty to overcome is that of similar scenes. A person reaching out to shake the hand of a colleague looks similar to a person reaching out to steal from a pocket. A hug looks like a grapple and a friend lighting another's cigarette could be perceived as a person being threatened with a knife. These events are very difficult to separate and analyse in isolation which is why it is important to consider the entire scene and previous activity within it.

Tracking People

A CCTV system that can identify a target by a unique feature can predict where that target will appear next on the system should it leave the field of view of a particular camera. Unique identification is commonly achieved by recognising an individual's walk or 'gait'.

Gait recognition is the identification of unique characteristics within our walking style. We each have a set of these characteristics that are almost as unique as our fingerprints. The gait of an individual is affected by external conditions such as clothing, the walking surface, injury, whether the person is carrying something etc. but the system analytics can compare the readings that it is receiving against known models and identify the individual with a good level of reliability even if the target disappears from the scene and reappears on another camera. However, gait recognition does not compare with biometric identification techniques such as iris or fingerprint reading but, given its ability to track without the need for cooperation from the target, it is sufficient to act as a powerful tool within an integrated electronic security system to track an individual across multiple cameras without the need for the views to overlap. This type of technology can be deployed in a live situation such as a surveillance operation but the power lies within the post-event evaluation capabilities to identify an individual at a scene and track that person's activity both prior to and after the event.

With the ability to analyse video content across multiple cameras, a system is able to apply algorithms to a wider scene of activity. For example, if the trajectory of a known target across a wide area covered by multiple cameras indicated that an event might occur, then the alert would be raised. This specific scenario would be useful in a city centre application where riots may be expected during a sporting event or political unrest.

Automatic Number Plate Recognition

Automatic Number Plate Recognition or ANPR is a specialised CCTV system that can read the licence plate of a moving vehicle using optical character recognition (OCR) software. The systems are deployed by police authorities to catch vehicles being driven illegally, too fast or without the correct documentation or even if the registered owner is banned from driving. Private owners use ANPR to track unwanted visitors, open barriers to known vehicles or track the arrival and departure of vehicles. This list of applications is as long as the users imagination. The software that tracks and cross-references the number plate against a database is almost limitless in its capabilities.

The ANPR camera is a specialised device that has all of the necessary features to clearly read the licence plate of a moving vehicle. In principle, a conventional CCTV camera can do the same job but an ANPR camera is not interested in a wide field of view or colour rendition so it can concentrate on reading the licence plate.

Specialised cameras have been developed to have high resolution, and a fast image capture rate with wide dynamic functions to cope with the high-contrast lighting caused by vehicle head lights. Many ANPR cameras have integral IR illumination and optical filters to ensure that they capture the best possible image of the number plate. The use of IR illumination takes advantage of the retro-reflective nature of most number plates, and the optical filters remove the visible light from the field of view. Retro-reflective means that any light hitting the plate is reflected back in the same direction as the source of the light i.e. directly back at the camera. Having an infrared illuminator located at the same angle as the camera and removing the visual frequencies of light enables the camera to clearly distinguish the characters on the plate no matter what time of the day or night it is. If the text on the licence plate is not retro-reflective, then there is an even higher contrast difference between the characters and the retro-reflective background which provides a clear image of the letters and numbers on the plate.

The angle of the ANPR camera in relation to the vehicle is important in terms of being able to read licence plates, and having the camera pointing directly at the plate is the most successful view. Steep angles of view will make the text on the plate seem shorter than it really is and the system may not recognise the characters. This means that camera positioning needs some careful consideration and low level bollard mounted cameras are common. The lens size also needs to be considered carefully to ensure that the license plate occupies as much of the screen as possible while covering the full width of the road. If an overview of the vehicles passing by is required then a separate 'overview camera' is needed. An overview camera can be a conventional CCTV camera.

The ANPR system grabs the images from the camera and reads them using a series of algorithms which locates the licence plate, takes into consideration the distortion introduced by the angle of view or the angle of the vehicle, adjusts the image for optimum recognition and then identifies the characters using Optical Character Recognition (OCR) software which scans the pixels within the image for known patterns to establish if it recognises a letter or number. When it identifies a character, it inserts an ASCII code for the pattern. An ASCII code is the American Standard Code for Information Interchange which is the standard binary code that computers use to identify letters, numbers and symbols.

When the system has identified the characters on the licence plate they can be compared to a database for known licences. This is when the functionality of the ANPR system becomes almost limitless. Software applications can take the data and alert that the vehicle is present to an operator, raise a vehicle barrier or record that the vehicle passed a certain point at a certain time. ANPR systems are deployed in many situations from law enforcement to visitor management.

Audio Challenge

Audio challenge allows an operator to talk directly to an individual or a crowd appearing on a CCTV camera via a public address (PA) system. The fact that an individual can hear a real person who is talking to them and responding to their actions is often enough to displace them. The PA system is not unique and public address is a whole subject in itself but audio challenge opens up an audio link to the field of view either when the camera is selected or on demand by the operator. With audio challenge the audio channel is linked to the video channel so that the two appear simultaneously. If the system is deployed on a perimeter, it is possible to arrange the PA horns (loudspeakers) in zones so that several horns can cover a wide area.

The power of audio challenge is not to be underestimated. Not only does the system give an operator the ability to disperse criminal or generally unwanted activity, it also instils confidence in the police authority to attend the incident. Having the event verified by video and challenged by an operator is more likely to solicit a police response from the local force.

There is however a poor relation to audio challenge systems which is a recorded message that automatically plays when activity is detected in a predetermined area. The system could be triggered by a movement detector or gate opening and it is often paired with a floodlight being turned on at the same time. These systems provide little deterrent value and, more often than not, annoy the local community through nuisance activations. There is some merit in that the first time it activates the message will probably deter any further miscreant activity but these systems are soon recognised as automated. At this point the value drops significantly.

Designing an effective audio challenge system is not necessarily an easy task. An engineer can learn about the technology involved and the ways to transmit and produce clear audio without interference. The difficulty comes with environmental conditions. Most audio challenge systems are deployed externally are and therefore subject to uncontrolled surroundings. Wind, rain, and snow will affect the acoustic quality of the environment and therefore the performance of the system. You may be tempted to design a system that is loud enough to be heard in all of these conditions but on a still night or if there is a light breeze in the direction of the local community, the system will annoy neighbours.

Chapter 3

Electronic Access Control

In the context of this book and within an integrated electronic security system, Electronic Access Control Systems (EACS) are, on a basic level, automated locking systems that know who can enter which area and when they can enter it. The system reads some credentials that act as a unique identifier belonging to the person trying to gain entry and compares them with an internal database to see if this person is allowed through the door at all or at this time. If there is a match and authority is granted, the system unlocks the door and the person can enter.

The technicalities within an electronic access control system are not with the principles and deployment but lie within the many field devices available, communications, encryption and within the multiple layers of programming that are required to ensure that only the right person enters at the right time. The system must be programmed so that upon presentation of a valid identifier, the system cross-references the credentials with a user profile that has an associated time zone to ensure that entry is allowed and the door is unlocked for a predefined time before relocking. If the door unlock time is too short, the system will be an inconvenience because either the person will not get through before the door is relocked or a 'door-held' open alarm will be raised. If the unlock time is too long, then the door is left unsecured after the person has been through it. Every transaction at the door is recorded in the system log for reporting purposes. Whether an access request has been granted or denied, an unknown identifier has been presented or if a door is forced or held open, the system records it so that specific events can be isolated or to see if any trends are apparent. Trend analysis is a powerful tool because it can tell a security manager a lot about their scheme and the security of their facility. For example, an increased level of unknown identifiers being presented to the system may indicate that an attempt to breach the scheme is in the planning stage. If access requests are being made regularly by someone who does not have the authority to enter some areas, this may indicate that he or she is behaving suspiciously. It may simply be that their job role has changed and their card profile needs altering but, either way, the intelligence of an electronic access control system is a potent tool.

Putting the programming and reporting aside for a moment, most of the time the electronic access control system simply locks and unlocks doors. When an identifier is presented to a reader, a signal is sent to a door controller. The signal from the reader contains a unique number that identifies the individual and this is used to lookup their profile held within the system database. The database is spread across all of the door controllers on the system so that it does not rely upon network communications to make the decision to unlock the door. This speeds up the process and also adds a level of resilience should some elements of the system fail. A good quality door controller can operate standalone without the need to communicate with the rest of the system.

The door controller either applies or removes the power from the locking mechanism depending upon the lock type, allowing the door to be opened. A Push to Exit (PTE) switch located on the secure side of the door allows a person to leave the area by simply pressing a button rather than having to re-present their credentials. A magnetic door contact monitors whether the door is open or closed and is used in conjunction with a timer to determine if the door has been held open for too long. If the door is on an emergency route, then a mechanical override to the system must be present. This may be an emergency Break-Glass Unit (BGU) that cuts the power to the lock or it could be a lever that mechanically withdraws the lock bolt. There are many versions and combinations of equipment around an electronically-controlled door but the basic principle is always the same. An identifying credential is read at the door, a signal is sent to a controller which decides if the door can be unlocked or not and the door controller is connected to a PC or server via a network for programming and advance system functionality such as reporting.

Security Tiers

As with any security system, proper planning prior to design is essential to the successful deployment of the scheme. If not done correctly, electronic access control can have dramatic negative effects on the way a business or facility operates. Equally, if not planned properly, the scheme will be easily compromised either by miscreant behaviour or by legitimate people bypassing the systems.

A set of floor plans is essential to the proper planning of an access control system so that secure lines can be drawn and different areas can be coloured to differentiate them in the scheme. Only a very basic system would allow all users access to all areas.

A complex access control system should be tiered to protect the inner sanctums of the secure area. In a business, this may be the communications rooms or equipment mainframes. This tiered approach is designed to allow those who do not need access to high-security areas to move freely around the areas where they are authorised to be but not allow them close to the inner hub.

To establish the security tiers, it is important to understand what is being protected, the threat it is being protected from and what the impact would be if the protected area is compromised. With this knowledge, a set of floor plans, and an understanding of who needs access to which areas, it is possible to form a control diagram to represent the principles of the scheme.

A control diagram shows the access control linkages between different areas within the building. For example, it could show the control mechanism that stops the general public walking onto a working floor of an office building. Another example is the control that stops unauthorised people gaining access to critical areas such as communications (comms) rooms.

The following example of a control diagram is for a multi-storey office building with a car parking garage beneath it.

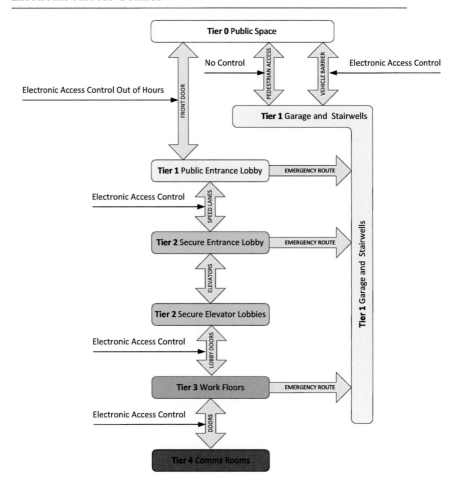

Figure 46 EACS Control Diagram

The general public can walk up to the front door and enter the lobby but would not generally do this unless they had business at the building. The public could also enter the garage area but again, normally this would only be if they had business there. Once in the building they can then walk up to reception and converse with the people there but they shouldn't be able to get any further into the premises. All of these areas are coloured yellow. A secure side to the entrance lobby has been established to separate authorised personnel from the public. People allowed on the secure side of the lobby may also be allowed on some but not all of the floors so the elevator lobbies form part of an internal secure line. This means that you can only leave the lobby on a particular floor if you have authority to do so. These areas are coloured green. The communications (comms) rooms are located on certain floors and in this example, they have the highest level of security and are coloured red.

You can see in the diagram on the previous page that everybody in the Tier 0 public space has uncontrolled access during the day to the Tier 1 business space (yellow) which is either the public lobby or garage. There is no direct route from the garage to the lobby so everybody has to enter the building through the front door. The front door is only electronically controlled at night because the business does not expect visitors out of hours. However, an authorised person may enter. You will also see that although the public can walk into the garage, only authorised vehicles may enter through the barrier. Tier 1 is segregated from Tier 2 in the entrance lobby by speed lane barriers. A person authorised to enter this area can use the elevators to access any floor but will need another level of authorisation to enter their own Tier 3 work area. A third level of authorisation is required for engineers to enter a comms room.

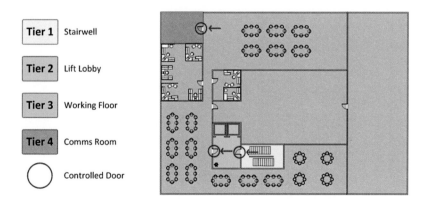

Tier 1	Stairwell
Tier 2	Lift Lobby
Tier 3	Working Floor
Tier 4	Comms Room
○	Controlled Door

Figure 47 Tiered Floor Plan

The control diagram allows you to plan the security tiers and it highlights weak points in the layout of the building. In this case, emergency escape stairwells exit each floor down to the garage. They are essential and although they are emergency exit-only doors, this highlights that a member of the public could get very close to a Tier 3 area without any obstruction. If one of these doors is left open, the scheme is compromised. This means that these doors will be alarmed and if activated, the event is deemed to be a high priority.

When planning the secure tiers, it is important to understand the secure lines that form the boundary to each layer. The strength of the walls, windows, doors and ceilings must be proportionate to the security of the area and must provide a complete line that secures the entire perimeter. The whole perimeter is as weak as the weakest point on it. A perimeter line that has an unattended open window or fire escape door is not a secure perimeter.

> *The proper planning prior to design is essential to the successful deployment of the scheme. If not done correctly, an electronic access control system can have dramatic negative effects on the way a business or facility operates.*

EACS System Architecture

After understanding the requirements of the system it is necessary to consider what type of architecture would best suit the application. The system architecture is the infrastructure that allows communication between all of the devices and determines how the devices are to operate. Over the years, manufacturers have designed different system architectures and further variants of them for electronic access control in an effort to improve the technology and differentiate themselves from their competition in the marketplace. A system that is dependent upon communications with a server and network connectivity may not be very resilient against technical issues such as computer or network traffic problems. It may be thought that systems in which the readers contain all of the intelligence to make the decision to open a door are more resilient. There are many issues to consider when designing access control system architecture and the fundamental rules are that the system must be secure and resilient. Secure in that any equipment located on the non-secure side of a door must not allow entry unless the correct credentials are presented, and resilient in that as many points of failure as possible are eliminated from the system. Equipment or communications failure means that the door might not open upon a valid credential being presented.

The conventional way to meet these fundamental rules of electronic access control is to have a reader on the non-secure side of the door which sends an encrypted code to a door controller located on the secure side. The door controller makes the decision as to whether to unlock the door or not. The door controller has its own intelligence and only needs network connectivity to the server for database updates and advanced functionality. The connectivity between door controllers and the system server is generally either serial data or TCP/IP via a local area network. Systems that utilise TCP/IP communications have the ability to scale up to control multiple sites around the world and if the software is organised accordingly, a single database can manage access control for a global company wherever the door and people are located. These systems are referred to as 'Enterprise' systems.

With the advent of IP convergence and resilient networks, access control systems are starting to adopt the principle of moving as many applications to the network infrastructure as possible. This will produce financial gains through shared infrastructure and software management. An Ethernet integrated door controller is a PoE (power over Ethernet) powered miniature reader interface with clean contact inputs and outputs that can control a single door. These devices remove the need for separate door controllers and they connect directly to the server via a local area network.

The design of an access control system is very similar whether the architecture is to be for a standalone building or enterprise-wide. The key decisions to be made in relation to the system architecture come from the operational requirements for the system and that of the individual portals to be controlled. Many of the key decisions to be made are fundamental, such as which side of the door or barrier is the secure side, whether the door needs to be read-in and read-out for audit purposes, and whether dual authentication is required for higher security.

A system that utilises a single identifier such as a proximity card or PIN number is at a higher risk of being compromised than one that uses dual authentication. Cards can be lost or stolen and PIN numbers can be seen by an overlooking person. Dual authentication minimises this threat in that a card reader with a combined PIN pad will need both the card and PIN before it sends the identification code to the door controller. However, this configuration is still not infallible in that somebody could see a PIN being entered and later steal the associated card. A PIN and proximity card system does reduce the risk of unauthorised entry by somebody finding or stealing a card but it will not stop a planned and determined attack.

Personal biometric identifiers such as fingerprints or iris patterns can be read to provide the system with an even lower risk of defeat but these are also not infallible and two different biometric reading technologies are often deployed to protect very high security or sensitive areas.

Photo challenge is a system where an operator is presented with a record identity photograph of the individual who has presented a card or biometric identifier to a reader. An associated CCTV camera is brought to screen to show the operator a live image of the person and then the operator can make the decision as to whether to open the door or not based on the access control system profile for this person. Put another way, the access control system does its job but a human has to make the final decision to let a person through. These systems offer a very high degree of security but are not practical in high-volume applications.

Physical Barriers

Having planned and considered the system architecture, it is now time to decide which devices and technologies will best meet the needs of the operational requirements. There are many mechanisms used to physically restrict people or vehicles from entering a secured area but here we are concentrating on those that are electronically controlled and that automatically open when triggered by an access control system. Generally, a barrier will have its own mains power supply and the access control system will provide it with a signal that instructs the barrier to open or let a person through. Whether the barrier is a large vehicle gate on a lorry yard or a pedestrian speed gate within a corporate headquarters, the principles are the same.

The decision as to which type of barrier is to be used should be wholly dependent upon the operational requirement (OR). This could be that the portal needs to restrict pedestrian traffic flow down to one person at a time, meaning that entry and exit is strictly controlled and monitored by the access control system. The OR may dictate that the pedestrian entrance is fast-flowing to cope with high volumes of traffic so a speed lane or multiple lanes may be required. If a vehicle route is to be protected then further considerations are necessary – the width of the road, the speed at which the gate needs to be opened, anti-climb or anti-pedestrian barriers on and around the gate etc. The security rating of the gate is important if it is to withstand a determined vehicle attack. Choosing the right gate for the scenario presented is more important than choosing the right electronic system to control it.

Turnstile

A turnstile is a common pedestrian barrier that has a rotating arm or paddles which only allow a single person through quite slowly and one at a time. They can be used to control traffic flow in a single direction either allowing free exit or no exit at all. They are available as half or full height which simply refers to how tall they are. A half-height turnstile can be defeated relatively easily by climbing whereas it is more difficult to climb over a full-height one. Full-height

113

turnstiles tend to be used more for external applications because of their robust construction which allows them to stand up to inclement weather and a limited amount of abuse such as somebody trying to climb over them.

Speed Lane

When people need to be let through a portal one at a time but faster than a turnstile it is possible to use a speed lane. This has the same functionality as a turnstile in that it is designed to let people through one at a time but has the added advantage of allowing people through quickly. A speed lane has another difference from a turnstile in that it can also let people through who are carrying a bag or pulling a suitcase behind them. More aesthetically-pleasing than a turnstile, speed lanes are often found at transport hubs and within corporate buildings. A bank of speed lanes in the entrance lobby of an office building can ensure that everybody who enters the building in the morning without delay can leave in the evening just as easily. Speed lanes are ideal if the system needs everybody to read-in and read-out of the building. Apart from providing a secure perimeter, the advantage of read-in and read-out is the ability to make reports on time and attendance or create a muster report in the event of an emergency evacuation. The muster report can be used as a roll call to ensure that everybody who was in the building has evacuated safely.

Circle Lock

As with turnstiles and speed lanes, a circle lock or pod is designed to let people through one at a time but with more restrictions. A circle lock is effectively an 'interlock' configuration in that the inner door will not open until the outer door has shut. The lock is usually quite small so that people cannot carry equipment in or out of the facility and some circle locks contain scales within the floor to measure the occupant's weight to confirm that only one person is inside the lock. This mechanism can also be used as a biometric identifier to confirm that the person who swiped the card is inside. There are some obvious disadvantages with the weighing system of verification in that some people would see this as an invasion of privacy. Although the system works between upper and lower limits, some people go through relatively rapid weight gain or loss. Circle locks are very restrictive but offer good protection against equipment entering or leaving a space and are therefore ideal for restricting the chances of robbery or sabotage.

Raising Arm

A simple raising-arm road barrier that comprises a cylindrical arm which raises automatically when presented with a signal to do so will control vehicles but offers relatively little restriction to pedestrians should they wish to cross to the secure side. An anti-pedestrian skirt which hangs below the arm will stop people from ducking under the barrier, and a similar construction of collapsible bars can be fitted above the arm to prevent climbing over as well. The bars hang vertically under, and if fitted, protrude vertically above the barrier arm. When the arm rises the bars continue to hang vertically, collapsing upon themselves as the arm goes up. If anti-pedestrian bars are fitted, it is important to ensure that there are no gaps at either end that would offer a way around the barrier.

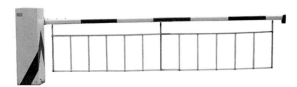

Figure 48 Anti-Pedestrian Skirt

Sliding and Hinged Gates

If the portal to be protected is large or requires a heavy-duty barrier to prevent forced entry it may be necessary to fit a gate rather than a more lightweight solution such as a raising arm. Vehicle gates tend to be more heavy-duty but there may be a limitation in the speed at which they can be opened. A wide road controlled by a single 10 to 15 metre-long sliding gate could take up to 20 seconds to fully open. In this situation it may be better to have two sliding gates, one coming from each side of the road. This will halve the time it will take to open the entire width of the road. This configuration will also allow a partial opening of the roadway for either entrance or exit. A point to note with sliding gates is that they need a space parallel to the fence into which they can withdraw when opening.

Bi-fold gates also reduce opening time by folding in the middle as they open. They also work well in situations where space is limited. Again, two bi-fold gates opening from either side of the road will halve the time needed to completely open the entrance. The gates slide on a track that is either laid in the ground or supported overhead. Some models are trackless and supported from the gatepost only.

If there is sufficient space, a standard swing gate may be the right solution. Whichever vehicle gate or barrier is most suitable, it is important to remember that sufficient space must be allowed between the gate and the road where the vehicle has come from so that a queue of vehicles will not obstruct the main carriageway. A good design will also allow vehicles that have approached the barrier in error to turn around and leave without opening the gate.

A sliding or swing gate can be powered in one of several ways. Gate motorisation can be thought of in three basic categories; openers, rotators and pushers. An actuator, or swing arm that pushes the gate from a fixed point, will open and close a standard hinged gate as if it were being pushed or pulled open by a person. A floor pivot motor recessed into the ground at the hinge of the gate will rotate and do the same job as the opener. The third category is the sliding gate motor which consists of a rotating cog that locks into a castellated strip on the base of the gate. When the cog turns it pushes the gate – forcing it to extend – or pulls it to withdraw being guided by a track laid across the road.

All automated barriers and gates of whatever type should include both warning and safety devices to alert people to the potential dangers and ensure that if somebody does get in the way, they don't get hurt. Warning devices include signage, exclusion areas painted on the road beneath the barrier, beacons and sounders. Safety devices for gates and barriers are usually either optical beams and/or a safety edge. An optical beam transmits an infrared light across the opening to either a receiver or a reflector which bounces the light back to a light-sensitive receiver adjacent to the light source. If the receiver does not see the light beam then the system will not allow the barrier to lower. If the barrier has already started to lower, the safety device will stop the operation and usually raise the arm again until it is safe to lower. A safety edge is a rubber cushion located on the closing edge of the gate or barrier. It works by having metal strips positioned on the inside of a hollow tube. As the tube crushes the strips they touch together forming an electrical circuit that stops the gate from moving and puts it into reverse.

If the automated vehicle barrier is required to have automatic free exit it can use a buried induction loop which registers the change in an electromagnetic field when a large metal object passes over it and signals the gate to open. Induction loops are made up from a loop of cable buried in the carriageway which is connected to a detector. The detector powers the loop which resonates at a known frequency. The detector then picks up changes in the loop frequency that is created when a metal object enters and disturbs the electromagnetic field. Upon detection the barrier will open. Buried induction loops are also often used as a mechanism to identify when a vehicle has passed under the barrier so that it knows when it can close. Induction loops only react to metallic surface areas; they do not detect people.

> *A barrier with a free exit induction loop and no anti-pedestrian features is at risk of compromise by an intruder walking under or around the barrier and sliding a metal sheet across the loop. The metal sheet may be as small as a dustbin lid. The induction loop will detect the change in its electromagnetic field, opening the barrier and allowing a vehicle to enter from the non-secure side.*

Blockers and Bollards

If a gate is not practical then it may be necessary to use a road blocker, sometimes referred to as a 'rising kerb'. This is a metal wedge that is recessed into the ground and powered by a hydraulic ram. In the up position the blocker will protrude from the carriageway by about 300mm with the vertical edge of the wedge facing the oncoming traffic. The whole assembly is encased in concrete which is enough to stop a car from crossing over. Some blockers will stop a truck travelling at 50 kilometres an hour but these are quite substantial.

Rising bollards are similar to blockers in that they are buried in the carriageway but instead of a rising metal wedge, a bollard is extended vertically to prevent a vehicle from passing. Whether using blockers or bollards, warning signage and safety systems are absolutely essential because they are not as obvious to a driver as a large gate. It is recommended to use a traffic light system in conjunction with rising blockers and bollards but it is not uncommon to pair blockers and bollards with a rising arm barrier so that the barrier becomes the warning device. This combination can also be used so that during certain periods the blocker (or bollard) can be lowered and only the raising arm is used as a barrier. This would portray a friendly, secure, yet welcoming entrance but when a higher level of protection is needed a far more secure and hardened entrance would be apparent when the blocker is raised.

Interlocks

Whether using external gates or internal doors (or even a combination of both), for higher security installations it may be necessary to ensure that one door or gate does not open before another is shut. This configuration is known as interlocking and is used so that entry or exit is strictly controlled. With an interlock, the chances of somebody following an authorised person in ('tailgating') is reduced. An interlock can also restrict the size of objects passing through the portal and provide a controlled space where a second form of identification is presented. It should be noted that it is advisable to install a communications system such as an intercom within an interlock just in case somebody enters and either cannot get out or does not understand that they will not get through until the door behind them is closed.

Interlocks do not have to be restricted to only two doors. The use of logic that creates AND or OR functions can be used to produce complicated multi-door interlocks. In a simple form, the logic can be programmed so that door A AND door B must be closed before door C will open.

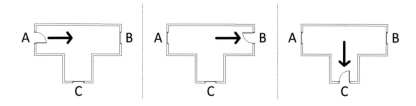

Figure 49 Interlock Configuration

Locking Devices

With the type of doors and gates decided upon, it is time to consider the locking mechanism. However, the first consideration is the strength of the door and frame because if this is very weak then there is no point installing a heavy-duty or high-security locking device. Apart from the many different types of locks available and the different technologies used, the next consideration is the holding force of the lock. Holding force is the amount of pressure the lock can withstand before it fails. Different types of locks have different holding forces and different models of the same type of lock will often vary in strength as well. Most motorised gates use the friction of the motor to lock the gate into place but it may be necessary to add an electric lock as well. Electric or electronically-controlled locks fall into two fundamental categories, fail-safe and fail-secure.

Fail-safe locks are used to secure an area but protect the people within it in the event of an evacuation. The power for a fail-safe lock located on an emergency exit route would normally be run via a break-glass unit (BGU) that will cut the power to the lock if the BGU is activated. This ensures that in an emergency, people can always get out quickly and that a technical problem will not introduce a risk that an emergency router door cannot be opened. A fail-secure lock would be used for higher security applications where emergency exit is either not required or has another means of mechanical override such as a handle on the inside which withdraws the bolt from the keep when turned.

Many electric locks contain self-monitoring devices to provide feedback to the access control system about its internal status. Combined with the door position sensor, a series of micro switches can monitor every condition that the lock and door is in.

- Locked/bolt extended, door in frame
- Locked/bolt extended, door out of frame
- Unlocked/bolt withdrawn, door in frame
- Unlocked/bolt withdrawn, door out of frame
- Tamper.

Maglock

An electromagnetic lock is often referred to as a maglock or magnetic lock because as the name suggests, the door is held shut by a powerful electromagnet. The magnet is fitted to the doorframe and a metal armature plate is secured to the door to align vertically and meet when the door is closed. All the time the electromagnet has power, it will hold the door tight. As soon as the power drops, the magnetic holding force will disappear and the door will be free to be opened. Powering a maglock to operate it naturally makes it a fail-safe device.

The location of a maglock is important to the security of the door that it is holding. Usually maglocks are located at the head of the door on the opposite side to the hinges. If the door is particularly tall or not very rigid, it may be possible to use the door as a lever by pushing or pulling it at the bottom. The amplified force may be enough to pull the armature plate away from the magnet at the top. A stronger location for a maglock is at the side of the door in the middle of the frame where you would normally find a standard mechanical lock. For higher security situations, it may be appropriate to install two or more maglocks on a single door.

When installing a maglock, it is important to always mount it on the secure side of the door so that it cannot be tampered with. Maglocks can be installed within an architectural transom housing that fits perfectly at the head of the door frame. This makes the installation a little less obvious and more aesthetically-pleasing than a magnet bolted to a door frame.

A transom housing is not always suitable because if the door opens in towards the secured area, it will obstruct the door from opening. In this situation it would be necessary to install the maglock using a Z and L bracket so that the magnet is installed on the door frame and the armature plate is lifted from the face of the door to meet the magnet.

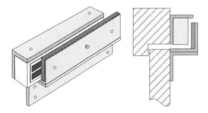

Figure 50 Z and L Bracket

Electromagnetic locks can monitor their own status using a built-in 'Hall Effect' sensor. A Hall Effect sensor is a transducer that converts one type of energy to another – specifically a magnetic field to an electronic signal. The device senses when the magnet is engaged with the armature plate. This is important because if a magnetically-locked door only relies on the door position sensor to verify that it is secure, it is possible that a non-metallic material has been placed over the magnet which would reduce its holding force while the door was shut and allow the security to be breached at a later time.

Shear Lock

A variant of the standard maglock is the shear lock. This device has the magnet and armature plate meeting in the horizontal plane. The advantage of this arrangement is that the magnet can be hidden within the top of the door frame and the armature plate mounted flat on top of the door so allowing the door to swing inwards and outwards. However, shear locks are notoriously difficult to maintain in good operation because a small misalignment between the door and the frame will stop the lock from working correctly.

Electric Lock

An electric lock, as opposed to a maglock, is one where the lock mechanism within the door is itself capable of being electronically controlled to allow the handle to turn and withdraw the bolt from the frame. These locks can be obtained in fail-safe and fail-secure models and can also be 'locked both ways' or 'free exit'. The locked both ways model has a fixed handle on both sides of the door when the door is secure. The lock is either powered or down-powered to make the handles operational depending whether the device is fail-secure or fail-safe. The free exit model only fixes the handle on the non-secure side of the door; the secure side remains operational at all times. The free exit type of lock must contain a micro switch so that when the free exit handle is turned, a signal is generated to alert the access control system to the fact that a legitimate exit is being made from the secure side. Without this signal, the system would report a 'door forced' alarm.

Installing an electric lock is quite difficult because a cable route needs to be formed through the body of the door. Ideally, this is done during the manufacture of the door but often it has to be drilled on-site from the lock position to the hinge side using a very long drill bit. The lock cable is then threaded through the door towards the frame. There are several ways to cross the gap between the door and the frame. An armoured door loop can simply hang from the surface of the door to the frame or a concealed version can be located within the hinged edge such that it is not visible when the door is shut. An alternative to the door loop is a hollow hinge. This type of hinge is a tube that can twist in the middle allowing the cable to enter from the door, thread through the inside of the hinge and exit into the doorframe.

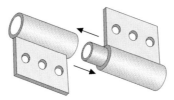

Figure 51 Simplified Hollow Hinge

Motorised Lock

A motorised lock is very similar to the electric lock previously described but with an added mechanism that automatically withdraws the bolt when given the correct signal to do so. This could be referred to as a 'motorised unlock' because a person wishing to gain entry does not need to turn the handle to withdraw the bolt.

Electric Keep

If it is not practical or necessary to fit an electric lock, an electric keep could be considered. An electric keep – sometimes referred to as a 'strike' – is the metal plate that sits in the door frame to receive the latch from the lock in the door. The faceplate of an electric keep comes away when the power is removed or when applied in a fail-secure version. The moving faceplate enables the latch to move out of the keep when given the signal to do so. When the keep is locked, the faceplate is rigid so preventing the door from opening. It needs to be noted that when using an electric strike, the lock handle must be fixed and not withdraw the latch when turned. A variant of this is when free exit is required and the handle on the non-secure side of the door is fixed but the one on the inside turns freely, withdrawing the latch and allowing the door to open. If this type of free exit method is used, the keep should contain a micro switch that operates as soon as the latch starts to withdraw in order to notify the access control system that this is an authorised free exit from the secure side. If the system does not receive this signal, it will think that the door has been forced open from the non-secure side and will set off an alert.

> *A fail-safe lock is powered to make it lock; if the power is removed it will automatically unlock. A fail-secure lock is the complete opposite of this in that it is powered to unlock, if the power is cut it will automatically lock.*

Readers and Cards

Locking the portals will secure the perimeter and it is then time to choose the most appropriate reader and card technology. There are many access control readers available that are used to read the credentials of an individual who is trying to gain entry to an area; from simple PIN pads to proximity card readers and biometric readers. The range is large but it can be simplified by categorising their function. Basic readers read a card number or accept a PIN (Personal Identification Number) whereas biometric readers read unique biological identifiers such as a fingerprint, palm print or iris pattern from an individual to determine their identity.

Card readers use a plastic ID card carried by the authorised person with contactless smart cards having largely replaced the older magnetic stripe technology as the most common form of identification for access control systems. They are relatively secure and can be used across multiple systems such as cashless vending and club membership. Administrators have the ability to print a company logo on them along with a photograph of the owner so that they can be used as a corporate ID card as well as access control credentials.

124

Proximity Reader

When a card or token is presented to a proximity reader, the card data is read and transmitted to the access control system. The card does not have to make contact with the reader for the data to be read; it will transfer the information across an air gap of around five centimetres. The system employs Radio Frequency Identification (RFID) which is a technique that uses magnetic fields to detect and transmit unique data stored on the card. Some manufacturers offer long-range devices that can read at greater distances. For very long-range systems, it is necessary to have either a very large reader aerial or a powered token and sometimes both.

The data stored on the card is encrypted at varying levels and standards depending on the manufacture of the card and the operational requirements of the system. Encrypted cards make cloning very difficult. Cloning is the term used when somebody detects the card data via their own card reader and replicates it onto another card in the hope that the new 'cloned' card will gain access to the secure area.

Pin/Prox

Combining a proximity card reader with a Personal Identification Number (PIN) keypad means that two unique identifiers are needed to be granted access. A valid read of a proximity card and an associated PIN being entered is required before the access control system will unlock the door. Using two sets of credentials to gain access is known as dual authentication and this technique reduces the risks associated with a lost or stolen card in that the missing card is useless without the PIN and vice versa.

Smart Cards

A smart card is one that contains an integrated circuit or 'chip'. The chip is powered by electricity through Radio Frequency (RF) induction which is the ability for energy to transfer from the reader to the card via an electromagnetic field. Once in the field of the reader, the card is energised and the data is transferred. The access control system can look up the access rights for the specific card presented and decide whether unlocking the door is an appropriate action. Smart cards allow for multi-use across a diverse range of applications. The chip can be split into segments to hold different data for different systems. This means that a single card can be used to access services from many systems. The list of possibilities is almost endless but for example:

- Time and attendance
- Parking
- Club membership
- Cashless vending
- Computer security
- 'Follow-Me' printing.

Near-Field Communications

Near-Field Communications (NFC) is a set of data transfer standards that has been adopted by the smart phone industry. The system uses a short-range, high-frequency radio signal to allow a smart phone to hold and transmit secure credentials to an NFC receiver so that a positive ID can be made. The advantage of this is not only that a separate card or token is no longer required but also that secure codes can be transmitted to any smart phone anywhere in the world almost instantly. This makes rapid global system management achievable from a central location.

Biometrics

Forming a level beyond PINs and cards are biometric identifiers which are the distinctive and measurable characteristics used to identify individuals such as facial features and geometry, fingerprints, palm vein, iris and retina patterns. There are far more biometric technologies than these but they are the main ones that are currently in use.

Biometric readers have had the reputation of being infallible and then had that reputation crushed when they have been compromised. Biometric readers are not infallible. This technology has produced some resistance from users because of perceived invasive techniques or privacy issues but a more common problem with it is that of mis-reading and denial of access. The reliability of biometric technology tends to be the inverse of the social acceptance of it. Fingerprints are socially accepted with some resistance from those who associate them with criminal behaviour but they have a relatively high false positive or rejection rate. A fingerprint system may be acceptable on a small access control system, or as a layer of a larger system, but in an airport with thousands of passengers passing through on an hourly basis, a high percentage failure rate would not be acceptable. Facial recognition is uncontroversial and socially acceptable but, equally, it has relatively high failure rates.

Among the various biometric technologies available, it is generally regarded that iris pattern recognition systems are the most reliable form of biometrics. However, while technology such as retina scanning may be more reliable it appears to have a greater social resistance due to its perceived intrusive nature. For this reason iris reading is now more prevalent than the deeper retina scanning devices. The reliability of iris reading was highlighted in a study carried out by the National Physics Laboratory in 2001 where it competed against four other technologies and won with the best false match and rejection ratios.

The false positive or rejection problems are compounded by the fact that biometric systems work on probabilistic results. It is possible to get variable results due to technical issues and degradation of data such as fingerprint damage. There is also evidence of ethnicity, age, sex and medical conditions affecting rejection rates. This means that having poorly-installed and maintained systems combined with the deployment of biometric technology at airports and other high-volume portals without understanding the makeup of the population being screened could lead to long queues and frustration.

No single biometric trait has been identified as fully stable or distinctive and biometric reading technology should only be deployed with this in mind. False positives and rejection rates need to be considered in line with the number and the makeup of the users of the system.

IP Readers

Some readers are classed as 'IP Readers' and one of the advantages of using these is that they do away with the need for a local door controller. They are powered via PoE and are usually self-contained in that they have input connections for a door sensor and push-to-exit (PTE) button and a lock output providing enough power to operate a standard electric lock. This type of reader has an on-board network interface and memory to hold profile data so that it can operate standalone if the network connectivity is lost. Although there are many convenience advantages of using IP readers, there are some significant disadvantages relating to potential security issues. The major concern is that the PTE and lock connections are integral to the reader and therefore located on the non-secure side of the door. Taking the reader apart and shorting out the connections will unlock the door.

Ancillary Devices

Around each access controlled door are a number of devices that provide the ancillary signals which monitor whether the door is open or closed, provide a means to exit without using a card and without setting the alarm off, provide emergency override etc. These devices allow the access control system to have the 'intelligence' to make the appropriate decisions regarding the status of the door. For example, the door position sensor triggering after a valid read means that the chances are the person who requested entry is passing through the doorway. If the sensor does not clear within a predetermined time, a

128

'Door Held' alert would be presented to the operator and/or a local sounder activated at the door. If the door sensor activates without a valid read signal or a push-to-exit signal then a 'Door Forced' alarm is raised which may have a higher priority than a door held alarm. The following sections describe individual ancillary devices, how they function and what features make a good device.

Door Sensor

A position sensing device must be installed at the door to communicate whether it is open or closed to the access control system. The system will be programmed with a normal cycle. Starting with the door locked, the normal cycle for legitimate access through the door would be door closed, valid read by the access control system, door unlocked, door open, door closed within a programmed time and after a set duration the door locks again. If this cycle is broken, an alarm will be generated. For example, if the door opens without a valid read or the PTE being operated, the system will produce a 'Door Forced' alarm. If the door is opened legitimately but not closed within the predetermined time it will initiate a 'Door Held' alarm.

Egress Button

Normally, an access-controlled door has a reader on the non-secure side to read the credentials of people requesting access but it is not always necessary to have a reader on the inside of the door to allow people to exit the area. In these cases, the access control system will still need a signal to indicate that the door is being legitimately opened but from the secure side. A Push or Request to Exit (PTE or RTE) button can be installed on the secure side of the door so that somebody wanting to leave the area simply presses the button and the door unlocks. This method of exit will not record who has left the area but it will record a legitimate exit from the secure side. If it is necessary to record the identity of people leaving then a read-out reader will be required.

The RTE signal does not have to be generated by a push button. If an electric strike is being used to secure the door and the door handle on the inside operates normally then using the handle will open the door. A micro switch located within the strike will be activated as the door latch starts to withdraw and this signal alerts the system to a legitimate exit. Alternatively, a motion detection located directly above or adjacent to the door will detect presence at the door and provide the RTE signal to the system. It is essential that the detection pattern of a motion sensor used for unlocking a door does not spill into areas that could cause the door to unlock unnecessarily. Ideally, the detector will only detect hand movement towards the handle.

Emergency Break-Glass

Some doors may be classed as emergency exit routes and therefore must have a mechanical means to override the electronic access control system just in case there is a failure that prevents the door from being used. This may be a panic bar or a paddle that allows the latch to be withdrawn by simply pushing it. Fitting a panic bar or paddle may not always be ideal in which case an Emergency Break-Glass Unit (BGU) can be installed. When activated, a BGU breaks both the positive and negative sides of the power to the lock. The lock must, of course, be a fail-safe lock so that as soon as the power is broken, the door is unlocked. Because the BGU provides a mechanical break to the power and without power the lock will not work, it is considered that a BGU is a valid mechanical override that can be used on an escape route.

Sometimes it may be necessary to fit a BGU on the non-secure side of a door. This can occur when the escape route is located on the other side – a lift lobby for example. In the event of a fire you would not use the lifts as an emergency route and if the escape stairs are not in the same lobby, you would need to get through the controlled door that leads onto the secured floor. Having a BGU on the secure side will introduce vulnerability into the system. The planning and control diagram that was generated at the beginning of the design process should identify these areas and make sure that there are further layers of security to protect the area. In the lift lobby example, people should not be able to gain free access to the lifts; this is often restricted by a bank of speed lanes.

Emergency Break-Glass Units should be coloured green to distinguish them from fire alarm units which are red. They should also be monitored for activation so that as soon as the glass is broken, the system receives a signal to alert the operator that this has happened. Relying upon the door forced alarm only, removes the possibility of an early indication of a door becoming insecure. Without monitoring, it would be possible to break the glass – possibly by accident – and not open the door. The system would not know that an unsecured door has appeared.

Although these devices are called break-glass units, many now do not actually have a glass to break but a plastic panel that depresses when pushed and can be reset with a key.

Key Override

In some scenarios it may be considered that the risk and consequence of a system failure permanently locking a door is too great and therefore an override device needs to be put in place. A key switch located where it cannot be tampered with can cut the power to a fail-safe lock so allowing the door to be opened in the same way that an emergency break-glass would. The key switch should be fitted with a tamper switch and monitored for operation, as with a break-glass although it will generate a 'Door Forced' alarm as soon as the door is opened. Introducing a key switch on the secure side of an access-controlled door introduces vulnerability into the system as it can be tampered with in order to open the door without authorisation.

Sounder

Some access control schemes are designed so that a local sounder activates at each door. This will go off if the system detects an alarm. A local door sounder is ideal for a 'Door Held' event which is probably quite innocent but the introduction of a sounder will alert the person holding the door open or passers-by that a system violation has occurred.

Anti-Tailgate Devices

Tailgating is the term used when one person follows another through a controlled portal without presenting any credentials to validate the entry. The first person presents their credentials to release the lock and the one following may not be authorised to enter the area. Even if the person following is authorised, the act of tailgating should be discouraged because the system will not have a record of that person entering the portal. If the system is configured to provide reports, they will be inaccurate if tailgating has occurred.

Anti-tailgating devices count the number of people that pass through a portal after a valid read is identified. The technology may be a simple, single infrared beam that crosses the door opening and counts how many times the beam is broken after the read. But a concerted effort by an intruder – possibly assisted by a legitimate card holder – can defeat this technique by tailgating very close to the authorised person so that the beam is only broken once even though two people have passed through the portal.

The problem of assisted tailgating managing to defeat an anti-tailgating device is greatly reduced by 3D or thermal imaging technology. These devices are located on the ceiling above the portal and can identify how many people are passing through as individuals or if the mass of the object passing through exceeds the expected size of a single person. If it activates for either condition the system can alert the operators and active a local sounder to indicate the violation.

Another form of assisted tailgating is 'Passback'. Passback is the act of an authorised person presenting their credentials and passing them back to somebody else to use in order to gain entry. Anti-passback programming of the system requires read-in and read-out readers on the door. The system will not allow the credentials to be re-read on the entrance reader unless they have been read on the exit reader first. This system is not infallible but it does reduce the risk of collusion to get an unauthorised person into a secure area. It also reduces the risk of cloned cards being used.

Door Controllers

In its simplest form a door controller is a device that sits between the door equipment (reader, lock, PTE etc.) and the access control software. The door controller accepts connection of the reader, door sensor, Push to Exit button and will usually have a couple of additional inputs to connect a monitored break-glass or lock tamper etc. An output relay will be provided to switch the power to the lock when a valid read is made. The door controller must be within a secure enclosure with tamper detection. Even though it has tamper detection, the door controller should always be located on the secure side of a door.

The door controller has a memory that stores all of the profiles on the system. A profile is the database entry for an individual which details where they can go and when. Having this information onboard means that the door controller can work 'standalone' i.e. in isolation to the rest of the system. Because each door controller on the system contains data relevant to its associated door, the access control server that handles the main software can go completely off-line without affecting the operation of any of the doors on the system. Any profile changes made at the server or door events stored in each controller will be uploaded when communication is restored. Having this data spread across the door controllers is known as 'distributed intelligence'.

Door controllers generally connect to the access control server via one of two communications techniques, either RS data or TCP/IP.

Secure Data Transmission

The electronic data that travels from the card to the reader, from the reader to the door controller and from the door controller to the access control server, must be secure to prevent tampering. If the data is read by a miscreant it will be possible for him or her to replicate it and breach the system.

The Wiegand Protocol for data transmission is common in access control systems but it is not a secure link. The protocol defines several characteristics of the card number format and the data transmission from the card reader to the door controller. More secure access control systems encrypt the data on the card and the transmitted data that is sent throughout the system. The United States Federal Information Processing Standards (FIPS) have documented minimum requirements for Advance Encryption Standards (AES) which are commonly used on higher security systems. FIPS 201 is the standard for Personal Identity Verification (PIV) which applies to access control cards, and FIPS 197 is the advanced encryption standard for data transmission. Encryption standards such as these make it much more difficult for somebody to tamper with the data.

Power Supplies

Power Supply Units (PSU) within an electronic access control system are categorised as Extra Low Voltage (ELV) i.e. below 120 volts DC or below 50 volts AC. These are the power supplies that feed the locks and door controllers. The power supplies that feed turnstiles and barriers will be a lot higher at mains (LV) voltage. Heavy gates may require a three-phase power supply.

A typical door controller will operate on 12V DC which allows it to be battery-backed so that it will continue to operate if there is a mains power failure. The same ELV power supply can be used to power the locks on a door but careful consideration needs to be given to the total electrical load. A typical maglock will draw 250mA but a heavier duty one will draw more like 600mA. This will usually be fine for a door controller PSU to support but if you have a double door with two heavy duty maglocks, it may struggle to provide sufficient power to hold the door at full locking force. Under these 'overload' conditions the PSU is likely to fail.

Another very important consideration for powering electromagnetic locks is the issue of Back EMF. EMF is an Electro-Motive Force and is generated when an electromagnet is turned off. The harmful voltage spike can return to the power supply and to any other connected electronic devices causing severe damage. Voltage spike suppressors should be connected to every electromagnetic lock to dissipate the high voltage transient safely before it causes any damage. If there is any doubt about electrical load or potential back EMF issues then a separate lock PSU should be provided.

Control Software

The electronic access control system software is the intelligence of the system. It communicates with the door controllers either via TCP/IP or RS data and manages all of the system operations from granting access based on profiles and identification credentials to system backups and integration with third-party software. The software resides around an encrypted relational database which holds all of the profile data and compares this information against system activity and time zones to grant access, alert alarm events and produce system reports.

The main purpose of the control software is to make decisions as to whether to grant or deny access based on access levels and time zones. Alarm monitoring alerts an event and displays the alarm location on a graphical map, also displaying the event time. The alarm element of the software can also display Standard Operating Procedures (SOPs) to prompt the operator on how to react to any particular event. SOPs will be specific to the facility and may change over time so this is a user-definable element of the application. An automated SMS text or email can be sent as a result of any condition arising within the software, giving the system the ability to be remotely monitored or make a call for assistance when needed. The control software operates a configurable 'cause and effect' matrix so that any output can be mapped to any system condition or input.

The access control software acts as the credential management application to enroll cardholders onto the system. The software captures and manages all of the profile data including identification photographs, biometric data, access levels, time zones etc. The system can manage visitors so that they can be enrolled and tracked separately from the main profile database. Visitor profiles are usually very restricted and have a short expiry time so that the credential can only be used for a single day or a few hours.

All aspects of the system programming are facilitated by the control software: from setting up operator permissions to creating cards, custom graphics, data import and export, right the way through to application interfaces and server redundancy. The control software is the brain and heart of an electronic access control system. The following table describes many of the common access control software functions.

Alarm Attributes:	The software provides the ability to configure how alarms are annunciated. This may be setting priorities so that one alarm overrides another, whether alarms need to be acknowledged and reset, whether they are emailed out or just show up on a map. The alarm attributes allow the system to be tailored to the operational needs of the facility, area or building.
Alarm Inputs:	Programing alarm inputs allows them to be named and have time zones applied to them so that they behave differently depending on time of day or day of the week.
Alarm Outputs:	As with the alarm inputs, the outputs can be programmed to be named and have time zones

applied so that they behave differently depending on time of day or day of the week.

Anti-passback: The programmable variants of anti-passback include specific cards, doors, areas and timing so that cards cannot be used to re-enter an area until a predetermined time has elapsed. 'Pardon' can be programmed so that an administrator can reset the anti-passback status of a card.

Areas: Setting up areas within a system means that it can have different attributes applied to different areas. One part of a building may have different time zones applied because it is a 24-hour operation whereas another may have anti-passback applied because it is a more controlled environment. Areas allow the system to be defined by zones which have their own specific requirements. People can also be tracked through different areas and separate reports can be generated per area.

Badge Production: This facility allows cards to be designed and printed and is often a bolt-on to the main control software. It allows the operator to design card layouts so that company logo, ID photograph, name etc. can be shown on the card. The badge production software often allows connectivity to a camera and card printer so that it is a complete package for producing an ID card.

Card Formats: The control software needs to know what card formats are being used so that it can understand the data that they contain. The software should allow for a range of industry standard formats from basic proximity cards to smart cards across a wide range of manufacturers.

Card Readers: The control software needs to know which card readers are being used so that it can understand the data that is sent to the door controller. The software should allow for a range of industry standard formats from basic proximity reader to smart card and biometric readers.

Challenge: Some access control systems can be set to challenge a valid read at a portal. As soon as the credentials are read, the system will present the associated profile details to an operator along with adjacent live CCTV so that the operator can see the person requesting entry. The operator compares the CCTV with the ID photograph displayed within the profile and if there is a match, the operator can grant access.

Door Configuration: The control software needs to know how each door is to be configured. Dependent on which system is being used, the control software will offer a variety of configuration options such as door relock time, door-held time, door automatically locks when closed etc.

Lift (Elevator) Control: The control software can be configured to work in conjunction with a lift control panel so that a valid read will only enable certain floor selection buttons to operate.

Nominated Card Unlock: This feature allows a controlled area to remain locked until a nominated person has entered. After that, anybody with standard authority to enter may do so. This feature is ideal for a highly-controlled area such as an armoury where the quartermaster must be present before anybody else may enter.

I/O Links: Inputs and outputs can be linked so that any input on the system can trigger any individual or group of outputs.

Group Creation: Access groups are collections of doors, devices or profiles that are grouped together so that they can be assigned attributes collectively rather than individually.

Guard Tour: A guard tour can be programmed so that the system will expect nominated readers or alarm inputs to be activated by a certain card in a certain order and within a certain time frame. If the tour is not done in the right order or at the right time, the system will alert and log the event as 'guard tour not complete'.

Holidays: A holiday schedule can be programmed into the control software so that cards become inactive during the times when people are not expected to visit the building or facility.

Interlock: Groups of doors can be programmed to interlock so that if one door is opened then none of the others will be able to be unlocked.

Maps: Graphical displays of the controlled area allow an operator to easily identify where an event has occurred. The control software can import graphics and overlay active icons that can operate field devices and indicate alarm conditions. Maps and floor plans can be arranged in a hierarchy so that an operator can drill down into more detailed plans from an overview.

Mustering: Designated entry and exit readers allow the system to identify who is in an area and who is not. At any point, a roll call can be made to see who is present. During an incident, a muster reader can be designated so that as people arrive at the muster location they swipe the muster reader. The access control system can then identify people who were in the building but have not presented themselves at the muster point.

Occupancy Limit: An area can be programmed so that no more than a predefined number of people can enter it. Once full, the reader will be deactivated. This feature should be used in conjunction with an information system local to the door so that the person requesting entry knows why they have been denied access.

Profiles: A user profile can be as simple or as complicated as the system requirements dictate. A credential is assigned to the profile such as a card number or biometric feature and the profile is populated with relevant data. Name, ID photograph, job title etc. are entered and then the profile is assigned to individual readers and time zones or to groups of readers and time zones. Profiles can be grouped so that all cleaners, for example, have the same access rights.

Schedules: The system can be programmed to perform scheduled tasks at predefined times. Tasks such as starting a guard tour, anti-passback reset, unlocking a door group, logging out visitors etc. can all be programmed. Scheduled tasks ensure that routine actions take place regularly and automatically.

Standard Operating Procedures:	Control software can be programmed to present information and instructions to an operator when an event occurs. These are referred to as SOPs because they ensure that whoever the operator is, the same standard operating procedure will be executed for any given event.
Tailgate:	The system may have an option for tailgate sensor control so that a device can be connected to count people through a portal and compare it with the number of valid reads it has received at the reader. The system will alert if more than one person enters an area after only one set of credentials has been presented.
Time Zones:	Programming time zones and associating them with individual profiles, devices or groups enables the system to have a different functionality at different times of the day or on different days of the week.
Visitor Management:	Visitor credentials need to be kept separate from standard profiles because they need to be managed slightly differently. The obvious difference is that they will need to expire as soon as the visit has ended. A visitor will generally have less profile data stored and have fewer privileges assigned. Visitor profiles can be assigned to groups, such as all visitors from one organisation are in group A and all visitors from another are in group B. Group A may have different access rights to group B. Visitors can be recalled and granted access for another visit at any time and can be tracked within an area. A separate alert could be generated if a visitor tries to use his or her credentials on a door that they are not authorised to use.

Reports

Reports are the hidden power of an electronic access control system because they can be used to identify who does what, where and when. A report can be generated to display the facts around a specific person or event or be used to carry out trend analysis to provide intelligence about how the security system is operating. Reports can be generated and viewed on-screen, sent to a printer or exported to a third-party application for further analysis.

Reports can be produced on most aspects of the access control system and the following list is only a sample of what can be generated.

- A list of profiles and their details
- A list of field devices and their status
- A list of groups and their members
- A roll call or muster report
- Alarm reports showing what events have happened and when
- Access denial reports to spot trends
- Alarm report to identify who acknowledged what and when
- Anti-passback reports to detect attempted prohibited activity
- Login reports to identify who has accessed the system and when
- Unrecognised card report
- Visitor management reports to identify visitor activity trends.

Reports can be filtered to refine the information being presented. For example, an access denial report can be filtered to show events in a single timeframe, in a specific area and for a specific profile group such as all cleaners. This will provide intelligence about the activity of this group in this area which may be that somebody was trying to access a portal that they do not have authority to or that the cleaners do not have authority to access a portal that they need to get through. With this intelligence a decision can be made as to whether somebody is behaving inappropriately or if the cleaner access levels need to be changed.

Report analysis provides the security manager with a detailed view of how the electronic access control system is working, how efficient it is, and if any trends are becoming apparent that would not normally be noticed if events were looked at in isolation.

Cable Installation and Containment

When designing an electronic access control system it is important to consider the physical installation to ensure that the security of the system cannot be compromised by somebody with a few hand tools. Any piece of equipment located outside the secure perimeter should be fixed using suitably-sized security screws. Security screws require a special tool that is not readily available and will make it very difficult to tamper with the equipment that they are protecting.

Cables should always be routed on the secure side of the boundary. They should also be protected by being installed above the ceiling or within conduit. This provides a physical protection for the cable but also separates secure side and non-secure side cables at the door. If a reader is removed and the reader cable is exposed, there is a risk that somebody could try to compromise the system by applying a high voltage to cause damage. Access to the reader cable could aid reading and replicating the communications data using sophisticated equipment but this risk is limited by data encryption. However, there is a far greater risk if the conduit that holds the reader cable also contains the push-to-exit cable that runs to the secure side of the door. In this case, removing the reader on the non-secure side and accessing the push-to-exit cable will allow somebody to effectively open the door from the inside without causing an alert. When designing the containment architecture for an access control system it is critical to have non-secure side containment for the reader cable and a separate secure side containment system for the remaining cables.

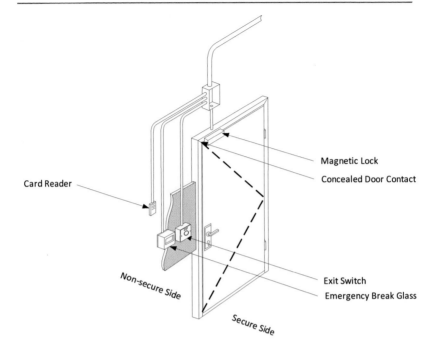

Card Reader

Magnetic Lock

Concealed Door Contact

Non-secure Side

Exit Switch

Emergency Break Glass

Secure Side

Figure 52 Typical Door Containment

Cables should always be routed on the secure side of the boundary. They should also be protected by being installed above the ceiling or within conduit.

Chapter 4

Intruder Detection

An intruder alarm system will generally have a dedicated control panel at its centre with a variety of detection devices attached. The control panel allows for the programming and operation of the entire system. In addition to the detection devices, the control panel will have annunciation and communication devices connected as well as a user interface which is usually in the form of an LCD keypad.

Detection devices include passive infrared (PIR) and dualtech detectors along with magnetic contacts, vibration sensors and break-glass detectors. A good quality detection device will be fitted with anti-tamper, and in the case of PIRs, anti-masking technology so that a shield cannot be placed in front of the sensor.

The whole system should be battery-backed so that it continues to operate if the power is cut, and external communications via a telephone line should be monitored for line integrity. If the line fails, a second form of communication should be available such as a GSM service.

Domestic intruder detection systems are available with wireless devices but a larger system or one that forms part of an integrated electronic security system should be hard-wired to avoid issues with batteries running down and electromagnetic interference or jamming.

IDS System Architecture

A basic intruder detection system detects a break in an electrical circuit that is caused by a detection device being triggered. Detection devices are cabled back to a central control panel using a multi-core signal cable. The cores within the cable are sized sufficiently to allow 12Vdc at 1amp to power a remote device from the central control panel. Three pairs of cores are required in the cable for a normal detector; one pair for power which is usually the black and the red cores, one pair for the alarm circuit which is usually the blue and yellow cores and one pair for the tamper detection circuit which is usually the green and white cores. Larger intruder detection systems tend not to cable all detection devices directly back to the central control panel but use data cables to connect a series of remote input/output (I/O) devices which collect the alarm signals from the detection devices and send them back to the control panel via a data 'leg'. A leg is a single data run that picks up a number of I/O units. A system may have four legs, each picking up 16 I/O units and each I/O unit picking up eight detection devices. This system would allow 512 separate detection circuits. If more circuits are required, a second control panel can be added which integrates with the first so that a single system is presented to an operator. An alternative to the data leg configuration is a ring topology which returns the data leg back to the control panel. A data ring configuration provides additional resilience in that should the data cable get damaged or cut, the data will travel in the opposite direction so that the I/O devices continue to operate.

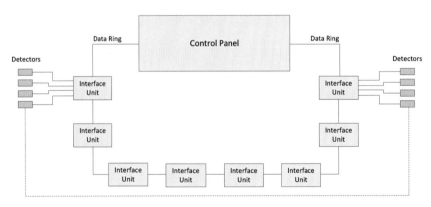

Figure 53 Data Ring Topology

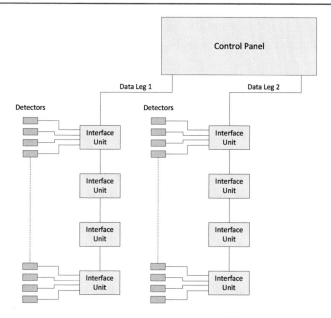

Figure 54 Data Leg Topology

A data cable also connects the remote keypad to the central controller. The remote keypad is the user interface which allows the operator to set the system when the area is secured. An alarm activation will be displayed on the keypad, indicating the circuit that has gone into alarm. The ability to reset the event is provided by entering a code. The remote keypad is usually a 0 – 9 number pad with YES and NO buttons to answer questions displayed on an LCD screen. It provides a portal to the complete system programming. An Engineer Code number accesses programming menus through the remote keypad that an operator or user code cannot see. This allows an authorised person to alter the parameters of the system.

An Extra Low Voltage (ELV) power supply unit (PSU) that would usually be rated at 12Vdc provides power to the central control panel and ancillary devices. If the combined electrical load of the ancillary devices is more than the power supply can produce then additional ELV power supplies are required. These could be located adjacent to the control panel or I/O unit so that the black and red power cores from the device cable can be diverted to the additional PSU.

Alternatively, some manufacturers produce I/O units with an integral PSU for powering the connected devices. Wherever the ELV power supply is located on the intruder detection system it must have a battery backup so that the system can continue to operate in the event of a power failure. A sealed lead acid battery should be connected to each PSU so that it trickle charges during normal operation but can support the system for at least 24 hours should the input power be disrupted.

An intruder detection system, when not part of a manned integrated electronic security system, needs to annunciate an alarm. A Warning Device (WD) such as a sounder or strobe light connects to the central control panel in order to activate when the system detects an intrusion. It is often the case that both sounder and strobe are connected so that they both activate when the alarm first goes off. The system is programmed so that the sounder stops after 20 minutes to prevent nuisance noise pollution. The strobe should continue to flash to alert the event until the system is reset.

If off-site communications are required to alert an organisation or the authorities, then an onboard communicator will send the alarm information to an Alarm Receiving Centre (ARC) which will process the event before contacting a named individual or the police.

System Parameters

Within the intruder detection system programming are a number of variable parameters that can be configured to tailor the processing to meet the operational requirements of the scheme. The following table describes many of the common access control software functions.

Codes:	This section allows an authorised person to add, delete and alter access codes.
DST:	The times of the year can be set so that the system automatically adjusts to daylight saving time.

Exit Time:	After the set command has been entered, this is the amount of time allowed for a person to leave the area via the exit route and close the door behind them.
Entry Time:	This is the time allowed from the point that the entry route is first activated to the unset code being entered into the system.
Lockout Time:	The system can be programmed so that it will not unset between certain times – overnight, for example.
Omit Group:	Individual zones can be grouped together so that the whole group can be temporarily isolated so that they will not activate while the system is set.
Omit Zones:	This allows individual zones to be temporarily isolated so that they will not activate while the system is set.
Outputs Test:	By changing the parameters within this option, each device connected to an output can be tested without putting the system into full alarm.
Part Set:	It is possible to programme the system so that only part of the area sets as opposed to a full set when the whole system becomes active.
Print:	A printer connected to the system can print out each alarm line as they occur.
Schedule:	Pre-programmed timed events can be entered so that the system can perform a print run of the alarm log for example.
Time & Date:	The system time and date can be programmed.

149

Walk Test: The system can be set so that each detection device can be triggered and a local sounder indicates correct operation. The walk test is also entered into the system log. This is used to test the system without causing it to go into full alarm.

An authorised engineer has access to additional parameters within the intruder detection system to enable him or her to programme and tailor the system to the specific operational requirements. The following list is not exhaustive but gives an indication of the types of parameters that can only be accessed by an engineer.

Bell Time: The duration that the external sounder activates for. Many countries limit this duration to minimise noise pollution from nuisance alarms.

Bell Delay: Some systems may require a delay before the external sounder activates to enable a pre-alarm response.

Exit Time: The duration an operator has to leave the premises after the set code has been entered.

Entry Time: The duration an operator has between triggering the first entry route device and entering a code to unset the system.

Omit: In engineer's mode, this parameter determines whether a circuit can be omitted by an operator or not.

PA Delay: An engineer can programme a delay between a personal alarm button being depressed and an alarm being generated.

Programme   An engineer can set all of the various attributes
Zones: that are available to each circuit, such as 24

hour, part set, chime, entry route etc.

Reset: If the intruder detection system goes into full alarm it may be necessary for an engineer reset to ensure that the system is fully checked before it can be set again.

Resistance Set: This parameter allows an engineer to customise the system by setting the end of line resistance values so that a saboteur would not know what the values are.

Soak Test: Circuits can be put on test for a set duration so that if they activate, the event will be logged but the system will not generate a full alarm condition.

Each circuit can have a set of attributes assigned by an engineer. The following list is a guide to the types of attributes available in most intruder detection systems.

24 HR: Twenty-four hour means that the circuit will go into full alarm when triggered whether the system is set or not. This attribute is commonly used for emergency exit doors.

Double Knock: A circuit set to double knock will require two activations within a given time period before it goes into full alarm. This is used to reduce nuisance activations.

Exit/Entry: An exit/entry circuit allows an operator to either enter or exit through a specific route without activating the alarm. If the system is set and the final circuit has been activated so that an entry timer is started, the operator can approach the keypad to unset the system. Deviation from this route will activate a full alarm.

If these circuits are activated without the final circuit being activated first, they will automatically go into full alarm.

Final: A circuit programmed as final will start either the setting or un-setting procedure when activated.

Normal: A normal circuit will be active only when the system is set.

PA: This a 24-hour Personal Attack circuit that will alert as a PA and can be audible or silent so that it signals off-site without notifying the attacker.

Tamper: A circuit can be programmed to be tamper-only and can be used for micro switches that monitor additional equipment enclosures for example.

Detection Devices

An intruder detection system has a wide range of technology at its disposal to detect activity that may be an intrusion event. Detectors are placed in and around an area to form detection zones so that an entire building can be configured as a single system.

Detectors can be categorised as active or passive and as parameter or movement detection. An active detector sends out a signal while a passive detector reads the environment by sensing information received at the detector. Active sensors include infrared beams and microwave detection whereas passive detectors include acoustic and passive infrared detectors.

Parameter detection is the process of measuring conditions such as open or closed. By contrast, movement detection is the ability to identify if change has taken place within an area or detection field. The following is an overview of the more common detection technologies.

Acoustic Break-Glass Detector:	These devices are finely tuned to the audible and inaudible frequencies that are apparent when glass breaks. Older versions could be activated by rattling keys on a key ring but modern high-quality units are less prone to nuisance activations.
Dual Technology:	Any single detection device that contains two different technologies which both need to activate before sending the alarm signal to the control panel is known as a dualtech. These devices are used in areas that are prone to environmental conditions that can cause nuisance alarms.
Magnetic Reed Switch:	Two small pieces of metal laid in parallel to each other can be drawn together to close a circuit by a magnet. These devices are used as door or window contacts so that they can monitor if the portal is opened or secure. The magnet is fitted to the moving part of the door or window while the reed switch (the two parallel metal strips) are fitted to the frame. When the door closes, the magnet aligns with the switch and the circuit is made.
Micro-switch:	This is a miniature switch with a metal trigger arm. A micro-switch is usually used to detect tampering by activating when a screw is removed or a lid is taken off.
Microwave:	This type of detector sends out a microwave signal and looks for changes in the reflected signal that may indicate a moving object within the detection field.

Passive Infrared: Passive Infrared or PIR sensors detect very low levels of heat given off by moving objects such as body heat. These sensors are prone to nuisance activation caused by convection currents in the air. For this reason, care should be taken when locating a PIR detector to ensure that there are no radiating heat sources within its detection field.

Pressure Mat: A simple device that closes a circuit after a load is presented that is sufficient to activate the unit.

Tomographic: This system detects disturbances within a radio frequency (RF) electromagnetic field. A network of transmitters and receivers creates an RF mesh that can penetrate solid walls.

Tube and Batten: This is an old but trustworthy technique used to protect weak areas such as windows that do not open and skylights. A taught wire is threaded through soft tubes that are supported by wooden battens. If the tubes are bent, the wire will break and the circuit will be broken. A similar technique can be used on a door where the taught wire is laced from left to right and top to bottom of the door surface. A thin hardboard cover is placed over the entire lacework so that if anybody crashes or cuts through the door, the circuit will again be broken.

Ultrasonic: An ultrasonic detector sends out inaudible high frequency signals and looks for changes in the reflected signal that may indicate a moving object within the detection field.

Vibration Detector: Vibration or inertia sensors can be mounted on door and window frames as well as walls or any other solid surface that transmits vibration.

Careful adjustment is required to eliminate nuisance alarms caused by normal activity around the detection area.

Window Foil: Another old technology that simply adheres a thin metallic foil to a large window. If the window breaks, the foil breaks and opens the electrical circuit causing an alarm to be generated.

Monitored Circuits & Tamper Detection

The ability to access any piece of equipment brings us onto the need to deploy tamper detection devices. Tamper detection is the ability to alert an operator to the fact that a piece of equipment is being physically accessed or damaged. Tampering is usually captured by using a micro switch that activates when a screw is withdrawn, a cabinet lid is removed or a piece of equipment is removed from the wall. Some systems use optical switches for the same purpose. These react to light changes either between a transmitter and receiver or within the enclosure generally. The tamper signal is fed into an input on the access control system which alerts when triggered. Ideally, the alarm input should be supervised so that it can detect an open or short circuit state as well as the tamper trigger. This is done by using a series of resistors that will provide the control panel with four known states:

- Open circuit
- Short circuit
- Tamper clear
- Tamper alarm.

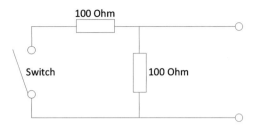

Figure 55 Supervised Alarm Circuit

In the example above, a closed switch would register 50 Ohms to the system because resistors connected in parallel reduce the overall resistance of the circuit. Two resistors of the same value in parallel will mean that the combined resistance is half that of a single resistor. Imagine a pipe with water flowing through it: two pipes side by side will allow twice as much water to pass therefore they have only half of the resistance to the water as that of a single pipe. With the switch open, the circuit only reads one resistor which is 100 Ohms. Therefore, a switch-closed reading of 50 Ohms means that the tamper switch is in place and everything is normal. A reading of 100 Ohms means that the switch is open and therefore the tamper switch has activated. If the circuit is cut or shorted together between the resistors and the control panel, then either zero or infinite resistance is recorded and either open or short circuit is alerted.

Beyond tamper alarms, many systems send regular polling signals that 'ask' if the field equipment is normal. Upon receipt of the poll, the field equipment sends back a signal in response. If the system does not receive the response in good time it alerts to the operator that there has been a communications failure.

> *A variety of detection devices will make up an intruder alarm system. Each device has a set of unique characteristics and weaknesses. It is important to select detection devices that will not produce nuisance alarms caused by environmental conditions.*

Chapter

Wide Area Surveillance

5

Wide Area Surveillance, as the name suggests, is the ability to monitor a large area and provide validated information in order to initiate a response. What defines a large area is open to interpretation but any facility or region that needs a quick response that would not be possible without an early warning detection system, pre-deployed personnel or vehicular response, can be considered as needing wide area surveillance.

The two primary objectives of a wide area surveillance system are to detect and track. But if the aim of the system is to protect an entire expanse rather than to just detect and track within it, then it is worth considering the seven principles of area defence. These are known as the seven 'D's, which are to Demarcate, Deter, Detect, Delay, Determine, Displace and Detain. The intention of this philosophy is to control the activity of unauthorised people before and as they enter the protected area, allowing a verified alert and informed reaction from the system operators.

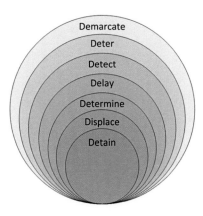

Figure 56 Principles of Area Defence

Security can be broken down into two general categories – active and passive. Passive security is the deployment of physical restrictions such as embankments, ditches, bollards and fences. Active security is looking out for events and reacting to them. This may be an electronic system or a guard on patrol. Passive security is arguably the stronger force to protect an area or facility in that physically preventing an attack is better than detecting and reacting to an event. The seven 'D's philosophy incorporates a combination of active and passive security measures.

The first principle, to 'Demarcate', will clearly define the boundary of restricted areas. Visual demarcation will generally be the fence line itself. The fence needs to be identified with appropriate signage to make it quite clear that this is a secure perimeter and that breaching this fence line will incur a penalty. Signage needs to be clear, concise and visible. Anybody approaching the perimeter, whether innocently or with an intention to breach it, must be presented with a clear message that will define the purpose of the barrier and the severity of the consequences if they breach it.

Effective signage can also provide a level of 'Deterrent' value that will discourage casual wandering into the prohibited area. Signage used for demarcation can also be used as a deterrent if the sign looks stern and is worded correctly. For example, warning signs can be used to identify hazards such as razor wire or dogs patrolling but these signs may not get the intended message across which is 'Keep Out'.

Figure 57 Razor Wire Signage

The illustrated razor wire warning sign has been designed for health and safety reasons; it could imply that the public are permitted to be in this area but they should be careful because they may get hurt if they touch the fence.

An effective sign must be targeted at whatever the people looking at it are thinking. In the case of perimeter security, thinking "I want to go in there" is the thought that we want to change. In this case we must consider the person's motivation because the higher their personal drive, the less likely they are to comply with the warning.

If the sign portrays a risk as opposed to a hazard, and the risk is getting caught, the sign is more likely to be effective against people with higher levels of motivation.

The signs below demonstrate a more aggressive message. They imply that beyond this point there are further security measures. The phrase 'beyond this point' clearly defines a line. Whether it is a physical fence or not, the line must not be crossed. Captions such as 'Unauthorised presence constitutes a breach of security' and 'Photography is prohibited' suggest that if either is breached you will be quickly intercepted by security personnel.

Figure 58 Signage as a Deterrent

Vehicle entrance points and perimeter routes need to have equally clear signage to deter wandering vehicles. Again, these signs portray a risk if the line is crossed. Vehicle signs can be larger and act as a first line of deterrence on the perimeter road for pedestrians as well as vehicles.

Figure 59 Vehicle Signage

'Detection' is the process of identifying and providing notification of a valid intrusion event or attempt. There are many technologies that can be deployed – from vibration sensors that will detect cutting or climbing activity on a fence to radar that will identify and track an intruder. A key point to remember when deploying detection technology is the consideration of the local environment; systems can be affected by terrain, weather, wildlife and vegetation. Detection is the first line of active defence – allowing an appropriate response to stop the intrusion.

Whenever possible it is better to 'Deter' an intruder rather than detect the event. Signage and visual cues can be used to put off the less determined trespasser but the higher the motivation of the intruder, the less likely they are to heed any warnings. Security planting, such as thorny bushes, can be used to deter people with a relatively low motivation to enter a particular area but be aware that heavy vegetation can provide a screen for a potential intruder to hide in or behind.

A highly motivated person will attempt to breach a perimeter defence whatever the risk may be. In this case 'Delay' tactics need to be deployed to ensure that the perpetrator is caught and either detained or displaced. Delays can be caused by the physical strength of a barrier against intrusion or by entanglement by something such as razor wire.

Electronic technology can 'Detect' and alert the security team to an approach or attempted breach of a perimeter. A detection system that alerts after somebody has crossed the physical boundary is not as effective as one that detects before a breach has occurred. There are many detection systems available but the most important consideration is matching the technology to the environment.

When designing a perimeter system of considerable magnitude, it needs to be considered that there will be an element of nuisance alarms. These will be managed, to an extent, by the technology deployed. However, extreme weather conditions and animals will cause systems to trigger a 'false' alarm condition. If the frequency of nuisance alarms gets above a certain point, operators become complacent and reset alarms without investigation. In order to maintain operator alertness it is essential to minimise events and provide a facility for them to be able to instantly verify or 'Determine' the event as it happens.

One of the best forms of verification is visually by the operator. If the operator can see what has caused the event they are instantly armed with the best intelligence to react appropriately.

Visual verification of an event can be achieved using conventional CCTV but it has its limitations. Darkness, fog and foliage can all limit the operational effectiveness of a CCTV system. Thermal imaging could be considered as a means to overcome some of these issues.

The final system is likely to be made up of a combination of techniques to protect the perimeter and using different delaying methods dependent upon the environment and the sensitivity of the area. Nuisance alarms can be minimised by using dual detection methods so that if either system detects an event it can alert the operator but not go into full alarm until both detection systems register the same event.

Verification of an event can also be made semi or fully automated by deploying specific software that analyses the content of a video signal to determine the nature of the intrusion before bringing it to the attention of an operator.

The 'Displace' and 'Detain' elements of the seven principles can be left to the procedural elements of the security plan and therefore fall outside the scope of this text. The whole seven 'D's approach to area protection allows for a considered security system that controls the events as they occur, diverting activity at the earliest opportunity but detecting and verifying real events when necessary. The technology deployed within this philosophy must be appropriate, proportional and suited to the environment in which it is installed.

Ground Radar

Radar technology is inherently suited for wide area surveillance. It sends out a radio wave from an antenna and detects the reflected signals that bounce off a distant target. It can quickly sweep a full 360 degrees, analysing the return signals to determine if there is any movement within the area. It operates in all weather and lighting conditions and can be designed to have an extremely low false alarm rate.

Radar can work over water as well as land; it can detect a variety of targets such as a person crawling, walking or running, and moving vehicles. A radar detector can pinpoint the exact location and path of travel of the target(s). A radar surveillance system can also provide masking of areas where detection is not required – in both range and angle – so that complex installations can be screened appropriately to avoid nuisance alarms from areas where activity is allowed.

This system uses radar technology for wide area detection of objects which are moving and then uses the precise location information from the radar to point a camera at the object. The operator is then presented with the location, direction of travel and identification, including the number of potential intruders all in a matter of seconds. This allows the operator to quickly have the detailed information that they need to determine an appropriate response. These systems can continue tracking an intruder with both radar and CCTV cameras after a perimeter breach to provide real-time assistance to the response team.

Radar detection systems require line of sight to detect an object which means that they are sensitive to terrain undulations and remote buildings that can cause blind spots. Unless the detection system is deployed in a completely open space it is better to install multiple low-power units than a single high-power version.

A major advantage of radar is that it can see beyond the perimeter fence and be used as an early warning system; which creates an amber alert if a person is detected approaching the fence line. The detection areas within the 360-degree sweep can be configured for different reactions to detection. Some areas can be masked completely while other can generate a pre-alarm or full alarm.

After an event has occurred, the operator can determine the nature and extent of the intrusion while tracking the intruder's progress within the protected area both on screen via the radar and with the fully-functional CCTV/thermal imaging support.

Microwave Barriers

These barriers generate an invisible three-dimensional, cigar-shaped microwave beam that passes between a transmitter and a receiver. They are specifically designed for external use but are subject to nuisance alarms being generated by animals, vegetation, severe weather conditions and objects blowing in the wind. Some microwave barrier systems use a form of 'fuzzy logic' to reduce these alarms by analysing the disturbance in the microwave field and comparing it to known models of behaviour before deciding whether the activity is an alarm event or not.

Microwave barriers are available with different range capabilities (maximum physical distance between transmitter and receiver). These are generally 50, 80, 120 and 200 metres. They can be deployed to create an 'invisible' barrier that encircles an area or can be used to fill a sterile area between two fences to ensure that nobody has entered the no-go area.

Fibre-Optic Detection

Fibre-optic detection systems can detect a single zone in a system that extends up to 60km. Point ID – the ability to identify the location of the event – can target a specific activation within a fibre-optic system to within plus or minus 50 metres.

Fibre-optic cables can be installed as a buried sensor system where the cables are buried directly in the ground or as a fence-mounted system. Vibration within the fibre causes a distortion in the light signals which is detected and analysed.

Most systems utilise standard fibre-optic cable which means that spare cores can be used for other purposes such as data transmission between outposts. However, the down side to this is the vulnerability of the fibre. It is not recommended to mount communications cables on a fence or buried just below the surface of the ground. An attack that damages the cable would trigger an alarm but it could also cut off communications to the other systems.

One advantage of fibre-optic detection is its immunity to electromagnetic and radio frequency interference. Fibre-optic cable is also completely immune to lightning strikes and naturally intrinsically safe because there are only light signals travelling through it.

Buried Pressure Detection

Two rubber tubes are installed underground to set up a discreet detection sensor. The tubes are installed approximately 25 centimetres deep with a gap of one and a half metres between them.

The system is based on the detection of pressure signals in the ground that are created by an intruder crossing the sensitive zone. The tubes are filled with pressurised anti-freeze liquid that allows the system to operate at very low temperatures. A crossing of the sensitive area creates a difference in pressure between the two tubes that is detected and handled by a transducer.

As with many systems, the received signals are processed and appropriate alarm signals are annunciated. Known pressure patterns, such as roads and railways, can be rejected which makes the system suitable for sites that are subject to high levels of environmental interference. The system is also immune to atmospheric conditions such as hail, rain or snow.

This type of system is available in a 'Point ID' version. Various companies are developing 'Point ID' which is a process of identifying the point at which a detection system is activated. A buried-pressure detection system can detect a crossing within plus or minus five metres, giving a maximum of 20 crossing points within a 200-metre protected zone.

This type of subterranean detection can be installed on either side of a physical barrier or in open space. It can be buried in a variety of materials including asphalt, block paving, gravel and grass. These systems are ideally suited for areas that need covert detection such as lawns and open spaces or areas that cannot have their aesthetics compromised. This form of detection can also follow irregular ground profiles both horizontally and vertically.

Buried Electromagnetic Detection

Cables that carry an electronic signal are installed underground to set up a discreet electromagnetic proximity detection field. Two cables are generally installed in a transmit-and-receive configuration.

The system detects distortion within its magnetic field and annunciates alarm conditions. Targets are detected based on their conductivity, size and movement. Smaller targets, such as small animals, do not meet the minimum requirements and are therefore ignored. Most systems operate through vegetation such as grass, bushes and trees.

Conductivity and distortion to electromagnetic fields are related to moisture content which means that these systems are sensitive to fog and standing water. Although they are ideal for following undulating terrain, care needs to be taken in low-lying areas.

In order to get the maximum efficiency from such a system it is important to install it correctly. That means that the two cables must remain parallel at all times and at the same depth in the ground. Prior to installation, it is recommended that a ground survey is carried out to determine the optimum spacing for the cables which is dependent on the ground type. Note that the ground conditions may vary around the site.

As with the buried pressure detection system, this solution can be installed on either side of a physical barrier or in open space. It can be buried in a variety of materials including asphalt, block paving, gravel and grass. This form of detection can follow irregular ground profiles both horizontally and vertically and has the advantage of detecting above the ground within the electromagnetic field, radiating to an average height of one metre.

Microphonic Cable

Physical perimeter security is an effective deterrent to intruders with metal fencing obviously being very popular. A determined intruder can defeat most types of physical barrier, usually by cutting through or climbing over. Many electronic security systems focus on detecting intruders either before or after they have entered the property. This can result in either nuisance alarms from legitimate passers-by approaching the barrier or late alarms after an intruder has entered. Microphonic cable detects the act of entry by sensing vibration within the structure of the fence. Sophisticated algorithms can analyse the detection signal and annunciate alarm conditions as either cutting, climbing or pulling.

Microphonic cable needs to be installed in a very specific way and cannot be installed on all types of fences. The fence needs to be rigid or taut to avoid multiple false alarms. Adjoining fences or structures need to be isolated from the sensing fence to ensure that spurious vibrations are not introduced. Gates also need to be buffered to reduce nuisance activation.

The microphonic detection system is designed to detect all of the typical signals associated with attempts to climb, cut or lift the fence. Wind, heavy rain and hail can cause multiple activations. It is advisable to install an anemometer to alert the operator to the local wind conditions but this will not reduce the incoming alarms.

PIR Motion Detection

There are many technologies used to make motion detectors; some are active in that they emit energy such as microwave or radar and some are passive in that they absorb energy such as heat or sound. A passive infrared (PIR) detector can sense temperature changes within its field of view as low as a human walking past. Unfortunately, they can also detect an animal and any change in temperature that may occur which limits their effectiveness when used externally. In order to overcome this, some manufacturers have incorporated signal processing and a second detection technology to work in conjunction with the passive infrared. These detectors are referred to as dualtech detectors.

Motion detectors are best suited to internal environments where detection zones are easily controlled. When using them externally it is important to ensure that nuisance alarms are minimised by installing them in confined areas such as adjacent to buildings or across gateways. Even with a high-quality detector it is not practical to use motion detection for wide open spaces when there are many other forms of detection available.

Active IR Beams

Active infrared beams allow an invisible fence to be created. The fence is made up of two units – a transmitter and a receiver. The transmitting unit sends invisible infrared light pulses to the receiver at the same time as a synchronising signal. The receiver will only analyse the infrared signals when the synchroniser signal is received as well. The receiver will not recognise continuous light – either visible or infrared – which makes it practically immune to direct sunlight or deliberate interference. Transmitters and receivers are usually mounted in a column containing a number of units that can be angled to crisscross each other and form an invisible net. Columns are fitted with anti-tamper and anti-climb devices so that they cannot be easily compromised.

For extreme environmental conditions, heaters, thermostats and fog discrimination modules are available. Although some manufacturers incorporate features to reduce nuisance alarms such as fog and animals, the systems are susceptible to problems with dense fog, snow and vegetation.

Active IR beams can be installed on either side of a physical barrier or in open space. They are ideally suited to vehicle entrances and roadways.

Combining Technologies

The very nature of Wide Area Surveillance means that a single technology is unlikely to provide a solution that protects the entire

168

area. Urban areas differ from open terrain as swamps differ from deserts. A combined technology system is most likely to provide the best solution. For example, microphonic detection on fences may be supplemented by infrared beams across gates that need to be left open. A buried sensor at an airport may benefit from microwave barriers across the runway. A ground radar system may be needed to protect the open area at the far end of the same runway.

The larger the area, the more likely that a diverse range of technologies will be required. Large radar systems will provide excellent detection across an open desert while sonar may be required at coastal areas and large river crossings. Gigapixel technology can survey a very large area from a good vantage point and satellite technology can do the same from a geostationary orbit. The list of detection and surveillance technologies goes on and on, with unmanned aerial vehicles (UAVs) serving as drones that fly over an area while transmitting images back to a control room. Scene modelling and image synthesis is at the cutting edge of detection of activity over a wide area. However, the more military style equipment falls outside the scope of this text which covers the general technology required to protect a house, an office, a factory, an airport or a facility that may form part of a government-controlled critical national infrastructure (CNI). Many of the systems described in this book are used for military purposes but are more often used to protect against crime.

Chapter
6

Integration

An integrated electronic security system should provide clear and concise information to an operator to allow them to respond appropriately to any presented event. The integration of the separate elements of the security system provides a single source of intelligence and verification to empower the system operators to make informed decisions. If the system is configured to integrate with wider systems such as building and network management along with local and global event mapping, it is possible to use the system to proactively predict potential security issues before they occur.

The integrated security system must be easy and intuitive to operate with a unified front end so that the operator does not have to jump between systems to get the necessary information. A Security Management System (SMS) can integrate disparate security systems into a single operator entity by drawing information from each system and presenting it via a third-party software application. This software presents a Graphical User Interface (GUI) to an operator which combines the information onto a single screen. The SMS operates bidirectional communications with each of the separate security systems so that simple commands such as 'select a camera' or 'unlock a door' can be actioned from the GUI.

Sitting above an SMS is a piece of software known as PSIM (Physical Security Information Management system). The PSIM not only integrates the disparate systems but adds the ability to correlate data to present events that may not have been immediately apparent to an operator. For example, two apparently unconnected events such as a local area network issue and an equipment room temperature alarm would normally only alert to the IT department that they may have a problem on the network. A tamper alarm on an access control door controller may only present a low level alarm that requires a maintenance team to investigate. However, if the tamper alert is associated with the door to the same equipment room that has the temperature alarm then a whole different story may be emerging. By combining logical AND/OR events, the PSIM software can see a bigger picture of what may be happening within the facility.

PSIM as a concept emerged because operators within security environments were crying out for better management of their security information. They wanted to be able to do with security data what every other business unit does with data; that is, to make intelligent business decisions. PSIM is a better, more flexible and much more useful way of managing security events and the information needed to respond to incidents. The system will collect data, analyse it and seek to verify it before providing a standard operating procedure to the operator to deal with the event. The system will log the event and provide reporting functions for post-event analysis. PSIM is simply the security version of the larger business tool of Information Management.

Ensuring interoperability across different vendors' devices/systems is a challenge. The physical security market as a whole lacks common, open standards. Thus, virtually any deployment requires the development of new drivers to integrate various systems. However, the capability to intelligently analyse and cross-reference incoming data represents a powerful tool in the security manager's arsenal.

PSIM principles may be used to produce better situational awareness, prompting better security and business decisions. However, alongside the intelligence of the system sits the environment that the operators have to live in – the control room. A suitable and proportional control room along with its associated areas is essential to the implementation of a robust security strategy. Operators will undertake a mixed range of tasks from VDU/GUI operation to producing reports and documentation. In order to achieve the most success from a security system, the control room must be designed with the operators in mind. Consideration should be given to the following:

- Security policy
- Security procedures
- Security mechanisms
- Task identification
- Time and motion analysis
- Socio-technical interfacing
- Proportional accommodation
- Resilience
- Disaster recovery
- Compliance with regulation and standards
- Disability discrimination assessment
- Health & safety at work.

The control room suite should be located in a position where it cannot be isolated or compromised as it must be able to continue to operate in the event of a serious disturbance. A briefing room may be necessary for management during a serious disturbance. The location of this room needs to offer safe access for emergency personnel and services.

Access to a rest room/kitchen should be available. The staff toilets should ideally be separate male and female but unisex toilets may be considered when space is at a premium. A disabled toilet facility should be available as required by the DDA (Disability Discrimination Act) assessment. A staff shower room should ideally be provided incorporating sufficient dry area for changing and storage of clothes while showering.

Adequate space must be provided for the services that are essential for the operation of the control room. There must be adequate height to allow for raised floors. Raised floors and ceiling voids must be secured within the envelope of the control suite.

Lighting should be appropriate for all the tasks being performed. However, consideration needs to be given to reflection and glare on monitor screens.

The control room should be designed as a low-noise environment with sound-absorbing ceiling tiles etc. The use of cross talk attenuation may need to be considered where ducts pass between separate rooms.

The ergonomics of the room needs careful consideration with respect to the positioning of monitors and display technology in relation to the operators. Headaches can result from any single or combination of the following.

- Screen glare
- Poor image quality
- Stress and anxiety
- Long periods of VDU use
- Poor posture.

The socio-technical interfacing considerations should take into account all of the above along with issues relating to watching images that do not change very often which can lead to 'change blindness'. Black screen technology and PSIM solutions increase operator efficiency.

Control room design has many facets from ergonomics to integration. Control room design, whether large or small, must form part of the overall security strategy and mechanism.

Chapter

Resilience

7

The elimination of single points of failure is critical to the resilience of an integrated electronic security system. A single point of failure is any device or connection that has no duality to continue operation should it fail. For example, if every element of a system relies upon a single personal computer to operate then the overall system, however well designed, is fragile. A power supply or hard disk failure within that computer would wipe out the entire system. The PC becomes the single point of failure.

The elimination of single points of failure does not mean that the whole system has to have duality to be resilient. A single point of failure refers to a device or connection that could compromise the whole system not individual devices. If a single CCTV camera fails, the whole system is not necessarily compromised since temporary measures can be put in place until the camera is restored.

Single points of failure are often linked to power and communications. Extra Low Voltage (ELV) systems that operate on either 12 or 24 volts DC can be battery-powered to prevent failure. The mains voltage will trickle charge the battery which can operate the system for hours or even days if the mains power fails. For higher voltage systems, an Uninterruptable Power Supply (UPS) unit ensures constant power in the event of a supply failure. A UPS is a bank of batteries that stores energy at mains voltage. The difference between this and standard batteries is that a UPS converts AC power to DC for storage in the batteries and then back to AC again for powering the load equipment.

Some individual pieces of equipment within an integrated system may be critical to the entire scheme such as a server or network switch. These items can be made more resilient than standard equipment by incorporating dual-redundant power supplies. The ELV power supply within the equipment converts the mains power to a lower voltage. It is quite common for these units to fail and render the whole device, and potentially the whole system, inoperable. With a dual-redundant power supply, two separate ELV power supplies are contained within the equipment. Each one is capable of running the device without the other so if one should fail the other will continue to operate.

Dual redundancy can also be used for communications links but it is important to remember that a cable that carries the critical data is also a single point of failure. For this reason, dual communication paths should run in different directions to avoid a single incident of cable damage taking out both communication paths simultaneously. Dual path power or communications may have to run in parallel at some points within a scheme. At these locations, a separation distance should be maintained to ensure that both cables cannot be damaged at the same time by a single incident.

Another form of resilience within a system is the ability of a software service or application to migrate when the host computer fails. A migrating server system has the control software installed across two or more machines. The software automatically monitors itself and if one element stops working, either due to hardware failure or the operating system freezing, the application picks up on another machine with zero down time. The new machine becomes the master server and the whole scheme continues to operate.

Even with single points of failure minimised, it is critical that control software, configuration files and databases are regularly backed up. A good back-up structure will have the ability to record all system changes on a separate storage medium. Recording changes only is known as an incremental back-up and should only be used between periodic full back-ups that duplicate all data. The third back-up in a resilient scheme is that of the operating system to ensure that any element can be replicated on new hardware if it became necessary to do so. Full back-ups should be filed in a hierarchical scheme referred to as grandfather, father, son. This method ensures that there is always a previous back up to use as a fall back should something go wrong. The first back-up recording made is called the son, the second back-up does not overwrite the son but becomes the new son, elevating the previous recording to father. The next time a back-up is recorded, the father is elevated to grandfather, the son is elevated to father and the new recording becomes the son. Subsequent recordings follow the same hierarchy and only the grandfather is ever overwritten so that there is always a father recording to fall back on.

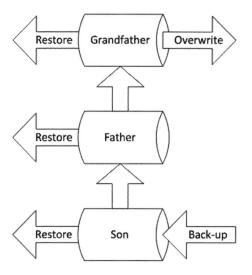

Figure 60 Back-up Hierarchy

A cable that carries the critical data is also a single point of failure. For this reason, dual communication paths should run in different directions to avoid a single incident of cable damage taking out both communication paths simultaneously.

Chapter

8

A High-Security Scheme

Imagine a high-security facility that has a large perimeter fence and within that fence is an open expanse of land used as a stand-off before the buildings can be accessed. The fence is a long way from the central control room so there is a gatehouse located at each of the two entrances to the facility. The facility is so high-security that only cleared personnel are allowed within the perimeter boundary. All access is managed by the gatehouses which can provide active response to activity on the perimeter and within the grounds.

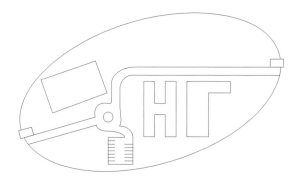

Figure   61
Hypothetical Site

The site has an internal car park and there are three buildings; one shaped like a letter 'H' another like the letter 'r'. The rectangular building on the left of the site is an administration centre for the facility.

179

The facility must be protected from saboteurs, whether they have criminal intent or are protestors. We can assume that the security procedures and checks carried out at each gate house are sufficient to reduce the risk of intruders entering at these points. We can also assume that enough distance has been allowed between the car park and the buildings to prevent damage from vehicle-borne explosives. However, there remains a risk that an intruder could penetrate the perimeter.

The first principle to 'Demarcate' will clearly define the boundary. Visual demarcation will generally be the fence line itself. However, the fence needs to be identified with signage to make it quite clear that this is a secure boundary and that breaching this fence line will cause a reaction. Signage needs to be clear, concise and visible. Anybody approaching the boundary, whether innocently or with an intention to breach it, must be presented with a clear message that will define the purpose of the barrier and the severity of the consequences if they breach it. Effective signage will also provide a level of deterrent that will discourage casual wandering into prohibited areas.

'Detection' is the process of identification and notification of a true incursion or an attempt. There are many technologies that can be deployed ranging from vibration sensors to radar. A key point to remember when deploying any technology is the consideration of the local environment. Technology can be affected by terrain, weather conditions, wildlife and vegetation among many other factors. However, whenever possible it is better to 'Deter' an incursion rather than detect the event. Signage and visual cues can be used to put off the less determined but the higher the motivation of the intruder, the less likely they are to heed any warnings.

A highly motivated person will attempt to breach perimeter defences whatever the risk. In this case 'Delay' tactics need to be deployed to ensure that the perpetrator is caught and either detained or displaced. Delays can be caused by the physical strength of a barrier against intrusion or entanglement by something such as razor wire.

When designing a perimeter protection system of significant importance, it needs to be considered that there will be an element of nuisance alarms. These will be managed, to an extent, by the technology deployed. However, extreme weather conditions and animals will cause systems to trigger a 'false' alarm condition. If the frequency of nuisance alarms gets above a certain point, operators become complacent and will reset alarms without investigation. In order to maintain operator alertness it is essential to minimise events and provide a facility for them to be able to instantly verify or 'Determine' the event as it happens.

One of the best forms of verification is visual assessment by the operator. If the operator can see what has caused the event they are instantly armed with the best intelligence to react appropriately. Visual verification of the event can be achieved using conventional CCTV but it has its limitations. Darkness, fog and foliage can all limit the operational effectiveness of a CCTV system. Thermal imaging could be considered as a means to overcome these issues. CCTV and thermal imaging combined with video content analysis will also act as a detection system.

The final system will be made up of a combination of techniques to protect the perimeter using different delaying methods dependent on environment. Nuisance alarms can be minimised by using dual detection methods so that if either detects an event it can alert the operator but not go into full alarm until both detection systems register the same event. Verification of an event can also be made semi or fully automatic by installing specific software that deploys a fully-functional, long-range camera to zoom in on the specific location of the event.

Any single technology, if suited to the environment, will provide a reliable detection capability. However, in terms of resilience for a secure perimeter, it needs to be considered that a single technology can fail or be interfered with. Two layers will provide resilience in that it is unlikely that two technologies would fail simultaneously and two layers can be used as a 'double knock' detection system to reduce nuisance alarms. Nevertheless, if one layer should fail or be taken down for maintenance then only one layer is operational. By adopting a three-layered approach, it can be assured that at any given time at least two layers will be in operation.

There may be unusual scenarios to protect such as perimeter crossings, inhabited areas and water crossings etc. Each one of these needs to be addressed on an individual basis and consideration given to the range of technology available. The following list is a brief sample of common technologies.

- Fence-mounted detection
- Power fence
- IR Beams
- Microwave
- Video content analysis
- Vibration sensing.

Using a combination of proven detection technology, the secure perimeter can negotiate any scenario presented.

A large CCTV system designed for long-range, day/night, pan-tilt-zoom surveillance can deliver one kilometer of recognition-level performance and 1,200 metres of classification-level performance in total darkness. To effectively perform to such capabilities, the system is equipped with an IR-corrected, long-range lens capable of 60x optical zoom. The CCTV system capability is enhanced using active IR illumination. Two sets of illuminators are provided; one for long range and one for medium-to-short range night imaging.

Thermal imaging cameras detect the thermal infrared element of the light spectrum which emits as low levels of heat from people or objects. The camera turns these heat levels into grayscale video for transmission into the closed circuit television system. Combined with video content analysis, thermal imaging cameras can detect activity over very long distances. These are ideal for our theoretical perimeter.

A video content analysis system processes the video stream from either conventional CCTV or thermal imaging cameras with various algorithms to identify a predetermined activity. There are many algorithms that have been produced and they tend to fall into certain categories.

A global algorithm is the most basic in that it is only looking for fundamental changes in the field of view. Another level is the tracking algorithms that can estimate true size and speed by knowing set dimensions. Classification algorithms identify the difference between different objects of interest. These algorithms can identify with a good level of accuracy whether an object is a person, a vehicle or something else. Once identified, the object can then be subjected to other rules such as trip wires, direction, loitering, appearing, disappearing etc. Behavioural algorithms monitor the scene over a long period to establish what content and activity is normal and then alert when something atypical occurs.

Buried fibre-optic cable can detect ground vibration and instantly locates alarm activations down to within one metre. The system tracks vehicles or footsteps and reports precise location, speed and direction of travel. The system only requires a single core of fibre-optic cable. Installing a multi-core cable will mean that a security wide area network will be deployed as a by-product of the detection system.

Ground-based radar detection uses radar technology for wide area detection of objects which are moving and then uses the precise location information from the radar to point a CCTV camera at the object. The operator is then presented with the location, direction of travel and identification including the number of potential intruders, all in a matter of seconds. This allows the operator, at his console, to quickly have the detailed information he needs to determine an appropriate response.

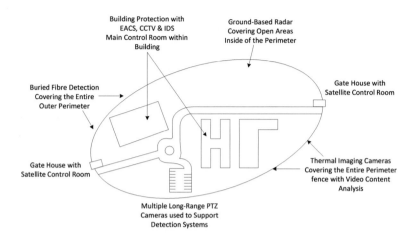

Figure 62 Hypothetical Integrated Security System

The combination of multiple technologies, wide area surveillance, multiple detection zones, distributed control and the need to intelligently manage the system dictates a need for an integrating platform. This platform should take in and manage the security system information but also be linked to other sensors and systems such as weather conditions, water levels etc. This gives added intelligence to the security team to make informed decisions about events as they occur. The ability to analyse and transmit this data across the security WAN means that a series of command centres can be set up to monitor and react to local events.

Assuming that it is not a very windy day and the local river has not flooded, a person approaches the fence of our hypothetical facility and the buried fibre will immediately detect the presence as he or she advances. This will alert the operators in the control room and the officers in the nearest gatehouse that somebody is approaching the fence. Pan, tilt and zoom CCTV will be immediately deployed to the location of detection to verify the event. The control room will be presented with the alarm event as a low priority and can see the CCTV image automatically appearing on the display screen. The operator can see that in this case it is just a dog walker passing by and cancels the alarm. Audio challenge public address speakers can be used to notify the person that they are on private property and should not be using the area to exercise their dog.

If the video content analysis, which has been installed on thermal imaging cameras located around the perimeter, detects activity on the fence line but the buried fibre has not alerted then the alarm is presented to the operators as before with support from a fully-functional CCTV camera. The alarm may have been generated by a heat shadow passing across the fence and the operator can cancel the alarm.

However, if the buried fibre activates and is shortly followed by a video content alarm, the event is alerted to the operators as a high priority. Fully-functional CCTV is deployed for verification and the operators are presented with all of the necessary information to deal with the event. The operators will be able to see if the fence is breached but even if this is missed the ground-based radar system will detect the moving object across the wide open space and set fully-functional CCTV cameras to follow the path that the person takes.

The early detection and the ability to follow an intruder provides the security team with sufficient information to send out a response team and manage the situation. Nevertheless, this facility is classified as very high security so the buildings are also protected against unauthorised access.

Protecting the buildings with intrusion detection and electronic access control allows the facility to be alerted if illegitimate access is gained but also manages the different levels of security within each building. Not all security breaches are made from the outside. Our hypothetical building requires a fingerprint read to gain access to the front lobby but when inside, there are further controlled routes that a person can take. The route to the restaurant area is free access once you are inside the building perimeter but the offices need a proximity card if you are to get through. They are on card swipe because they need to be controlled but do not warrant a higher security that uses biometrics to validate the person trying to gain entry. However, to get through to the data hall is another matter. A circle lock ensures that only one person enters at a time and that they are not carrying any large equipment either in or out. The circle lock is accessed via an iris read which is relatively slow but the data hall warrants the high security and controlled entry that this technology provides.

Once in the data hall, engineers can access their allocated equipment cabinets via a thumb or fingerprint that unlocks the enclosure door. The whole area needs to be open-plan so that the air can be cooled but an engineer is only allowed to visit his or her own equipment. Facial recognition CCTV located in each aisle will alert if somebody enters an aisle that they do not have authority to access. Video content analysis in each aisle also alerts if something is left behind or is removed.

The only people that are allowed anywhere within the data hall are the maintenance engineers. These people are registered with the facial recognition software for all areas and need to present a further iris read to access the plant rooms.

The whole system is integrated with CCTV throughout the building so that if any unusual event is registered, the control room will be alerted with video verification. All CCTV activity is recorded with pre and post-alarm recordings being presented with live video verification so that the operator can see what was happening just before the activity, followed by what caused the event and what happened immediately afterwards. This facility is essential if alarm events start to queue up.

The control room is ergonomically designed so that the security operators have all information to hand when necessary. The alarm monitor screens are usually left blank so that it is immediately obvious when a new verification image comes to screen. Other monitors and sections on a video wall are used for video patrols and general observation. An officer can be tracked on CCTV and on a graphic map as they make a guard tour presenting an access card to readers around the building. The map presents where they have been and where they should go next but if a reader is missed or swiped out of order, the control room is alerted.

In the background, the integrated electronic security system is monitoring events throughout the facility. Most of these are logged in the file but not alerted to the operators because they are mundane events such as access denied or incorrect credentials. This information provides the data for some powerful trend analysis to take place. A PSIM application enables the cause and effect relationship between detection device and CCTV verification but it also searches the event history for unusual patterns such as several attempts to enter a high-security area by somebody who does not have authority and the finding that that person has had an access denied within the high-security area. This information suggests that the person has been trying to gain entry and has succeeded at least once but been blocked by the next layer of defence. This essential information may have been missed by the control room if it were not for the constant analysis behind the scenes of the system.

News feeds into the control room provide the operators with intelligence on advanced weather warnings and potential targeted activity such as protestors or demonstrations in the area. The PSIM system takes information from a variety of sources to analyse time-framed events in order to predict future activity. The system will know that if the fence is breached and the target is tracked on a certain trajectory, how long it will take to reach any one of the buildings, allowing a lock-down procedure to be initiated.

This hypothetical scheme is a mixture of some of the technologies described in this book. There are countless combinations and configurations that can be deployed to provide an effective and proportional security system. The final scheme will be a result of the operational requirements exercise carried out before any design work is done. This scheme is for a fictional high-security site which is why it contains some very expensive technology such as iris readers and facial recognition. You would not expect to find this on all sites. A public access industrial estate, for example, may include CCTV and external detection but it is unlikely to warrant facial recognition.

Chapter
9

System Commissioning

The commissioning process will verify that a newly-installed system meets both the technical performance of the selected equipment and the operational requirements set out in the early stages of design. It is important to review the original performance specification and operational requirements documentation prior to writing a commissioning plan.

The commissioning of any system is split into two categories – components and complete system. Each device or component must be commissioned in its own right before the overall system can be commissioned.

Each camera within the CCTV system must be checked to ensure that the correct lens has been installed, the focus and back focus have been set, peak and average light levels set on the lens etc. These settings are usually carried out with the aid of a hand-held test monitor or laptop computer so that the camera can be configured locally. To set the camera for night-time operation, a neutral density filter can be placed in front of the lens. The filter is made up from a series of neutral colour coatings which get less transparent towards the middle of concentric circles. They allow the amount of light at the camera CCD chip to be reduced without affecting the composition of the image.

If the camera has a zoom lens, it is important to adjust the back focus to ensure that the image stays in focus throughout the zoom track.

Cables should be 'Dead Tested' prior to going live to ensure that there are no breaks or short circuits between cores. Once powered up, the voltage levels at each device should be measured and recorded along with loop resistances for detection cables. Video signal levels should be measured at the control equipment and documented.

Each telemetry function of fully-functional cameras should be tested along with presets, end stops and privacy zones.

The control equipment should be configured with synchronised time and date as well as camera titles. Each element of the control equipment must be programmed to fulfill its role within the system such as dwell times for sequencing images and master/slave relationships for duel control. User logins must be set.

Digital recorders are to be configured for normal and alarm condition record rates. Any motion activation settings should be configured for optimum operation.

The audio from each scene should be checked for clarity and video/audio analytics should be programmed and fully tested.

All detection devices are to be checked to ensure that they are operating as expected. A 'Walk Test' must be carried out to verify the operation of each device. The test should try and defeat the detection to prove that there are no vulnerabilities in the scheme. Sensitivity adjustments should be set to provide optimum performance with minimum nuisance alarms. It is also important to ensure that detectors do not pick up outside of the field of view of the associated camera.

With all of the system components individually commissioned, it is necessary to commission the system as a whole. This process involves operating the system from the control location to ensure that each item of equipment fulfills the specific category of the operational requirements document. Alarm activations that interact to switch live images to a display monitor and increasing record times are to be checked for correct operation. This relationship between event and system reaction is known as 'Cause and Effect'. All of the fields of view should be checked during the day and night and the system configuration information should be documented to provide a record for future testing and re-commissioning if necessary.

Reference images should be taken and stored from each camera during the day and at night after the commissioning process has been completed. These will provide a record of the fields of view for future testing.

A minimum of seven days should be set aside at the end of the commissioning process to allow an environmental soak test to be carried out. This will enable the system to stabilise within its environment. Also, it is generally expected that if a device is going to fail, it will do so during this initial operational period.

The following is a selection of sample documentation that can be used to record the system status during the commissioning process. Ideally, each form should have a signature on it when complete to verify that the performance criteria had been met.

Sample CCTV Commissioning Documentation

CCTV COMMISSIONING RECORD – FIXED POSTION CAMERA		

Project Reference:	Project Name:	
Point Identification:	Location:	
Tested by:	Date:	
Witnessed by:	Date:	

Device Type:		
Field of View:		
	YES	NO
Correct devices as per specification?		
Correct housing and brackets as per specification?		
Anti-tamper screws fitted?		
Quality workmanship, tidy workspace?		
Cables labelled?		
Connection to earth?		
Correct supply voltage?		
Environmental control operational (heater/fan)?		
Tamper detection operational?		
Focus and zoom correct?		
Iris set/auto iris functioning?		
Back focus set?		
Backlight compensation set?		
Colour rendering correct?		
Day/night changeover operational?		
Low-light operation checked?		
Signal transmission operational?		

CCTV COMMISSIONING RECORD – PTZ CAMERA

Project Reference:		Project Name:	
Point Identification:		Location:	
Tested by:		Date:	
Witnessed by:		Date:	

Device Type:	
Field of View:	
Receiver address	

	YES	NO
Correct devices as per specification?		
Correct housing and brackets as per specification?		
Anti-tamper screws fitted?		
Quality workmanship, tidy workspace?		
Cables labelled?		
Connection to earth?		
Correct supply voltage?		
Environmental control operational (heater/fan)?		
Tamper detection operational?		
Iris/auto iris functioning?		
Back focus set/zoom tracked?		
Backlight compensation set?		
Colour rendering correct?		
Day/night changeover operational?		
Low-light operation checked?		
Pan left? Pan right?		
Tilt up? Tilt down?		
Mechanical/electronic stops set?		
Privacy zones set?		
Wash/wipe functional?		
Support illumination operating?		
Receiver test modes functioning?		
Signal transmission operational?		

CCTV COMMISSIONING RECORD – DVR/NVR

Project Reference:	Project Name:
Point Identification:	Location:
Tested by:	Date:
Witnessed by:	Date:

Device Type:	
Software Version:	
Serial Number:	
IP Address:	
Subnet mask:	
Gateway:	

	YES	NO
Correct devices as per specification?		
Quality workmanship, tidy workspace?		
Cables labelled?		
Connection to earth?		
Correct supply voltage?		
Environmental control operational (heater/fan)?		
All cameras connected and recognised?		
User permissions programmed?		
Motion detection/analytics programmed?		
Record function operational?		
Video search functional?		
Motion search functional?		
Video export functional?		
Alarm recording functional?		
Alarm monitor pop-up functional?		
Video loss alarm operational?		
Auto restart and record on power loss/resume?		
Connects to remote review suite?		
Integration with external devices programmed?		

CCTV COMMISSIONING RECORD – DETECTOR

Project Reference:	Project Name:	
Point Identification:	Location:	
Tested by:	Date:	
Witnessed by:	Date:	

Device Type:		
	YES	NO
Correct device as per specification?		
Correct housing and brackets as per specification?		
Anti-tamper screws fitted?		
Quality workmanship, tidy workspace?		
Cables labelled?		
Correct supply voltage?		
Environmental control operational (heater/fan)?		
Walk test detection?		
Run test detection?		
Crawl test detection?		
Creep zone detection?		
Double knock functioning?		
Obscured alarm functional?		
Does detection extend beyond field of view?		

Sample EACS Commissioning Documentation

EACS COMMISSIONING RECORD - FIELD EQUIPMENT		
Project Reference:	Project Name:	
Point Identification:	Location:	
Tested by:	Date:	
Witnessed by:	Date:	
Device Type:		
Software Version:		
Serial Number:		
IP Address:		
Subnet mask:		
Gateway:		
	YES	NO
Correct devices as per specification?		
Correct housing and brackets as per specification?		
Anti-tamper devices fitted?		
Anti-tamper screws fitted?		
Quality workmanship, tidy workspace?		
Cables labelled?		
Connection to earth?		
Correct supply voltage?		
Lock suppression fitted?		
All ancillary devices connected?		
Communications operational?		
Backup battery fitted?		

EACS COMMISSIONING RECORD - ANCILLARY EQUIPMENT

Project Reference:	Project Name:	
Point Identification:	Location:	
Tested by:	Date:	
Witnessed by:	Date:	

Device Types:			
Serial Numbers:			
		YES	NO
Correct devices as per specification?			
Correct housing and brackets as per specification?			
Anti-tamper devices fitted?			
Anti-tamper screws fitted?			
Quality workmanship, tidy workspace?			
Cables labelled?			
Connection to earth?			
Correct supply voltage?			
BGU cuts both sides of power to lock?			
PTE operational?			
Reader in operational?			
Reader out operational?			
Lock power correct?			
Lock suppression fitted?			
Lock operational?			
Valid read?			
Card declined?			
Door held?			
Door forced?			
Local sounders/indicators operational?			

Sample IDS Commissioning Documentation

IDS COMMISSIONING RECORD – PARAMETER RECORD	
Project Reference:	Project Name:
Tested by:	Date:
Witnessed by:	Date:
Device Type:	
Serial Number:	
Zone Identification:	
Location:	
Area:	
Type:	
Attributes:	
Make:	
Model:	
Circuit Ω:	
Voltage:	
EoL Location:	
SAB Cutout Time:	
Exit Time:	
Entry Time:	

IDS COMMISSIONING RECORD - CONTROL EQUIPMENT

Project Reference:	Project Name:
Point Identification:	Location:
Tested by:	Date:
Witnessed by:	Date:

Device Type:	
Software Version:	
Serial Number:	
IP Address:	
Subnet mask:	
Gateway:	

	YES	NO
Correct devices as per specification?		
Correct housing and brackets as per specification?		
Anti-tamper devices fitted?		
Anti-tamper screws fitted?		
Quality workmanship, tidy workspace?		
Cables labelled?		
Connection to earth?		
Correct supply voltage?		
All ancillary devices connected?		
Communications operational?		
Backup battery fitted?		

IDS COMMISSIONING RECORD - DETECTION EQUIPMENT		
Project Reference:	Project Name:	
Point Identification:	Location:	
Tested by:	Date:	
Witnessed by:	Date:	
Device Type:		
Serial Number:		
	YES	NO
Correct devices as per specification?		
Correct housing and brackets as per specification?		
Anti-tamper devices fitted?		
Anti-tamper screws fitted?		
Quality workmanship, tidy workspace?		
Cables labelled?		
Correct supply voltage?		
Detection/walk test.		

Chapter

10

System Maintenance

Routine or periodic preventative maintenance (PPM) is a set sequence of tasks intended to ensure continued performance and safe operation of the system. The frequency of the maintenance is dependent on the nature of the system. A small system with a few internal static cameras and a DVR will require less preventative maintenance than one with multiple external fully-functional cameras and centralised video archiving. Generally, an annual maintenance visit is sufficient for any small system but if it is subject to adverse conditions or if the system is very large, then more regular visits may be necessary.

The maintenance programme must be fully documented with a list of tasks specific for the system, their methodology and associated frequency. The documentation should be supported with test forms to log readings and provide a detailed record of the maintenance visit.

At the end of the maintenance visit a conditions report should be generated along with the supporting test records. Any minor repairs deemed necessary such as the tightening of bolts or electronic adjustments should be carried out as part of the maintenance visit.

CCTV Check List

The following check lists are provided for guidance and are not exhaustive. Always refer to the manufacturer's literature for further guidance.

- General
  - Check that the system is in accordance with the specification

- o Check that all warning labels are in place
- o Check that all cables and containment are correctly supported
- o Check all equipment fixings are secure
- o Check that all glands and seals are in good condition.

- Static Camera
  - o Check the camera assembly to ensure that it has no signs of damage, corrosion or water ingress
  - o Check the bracket and fixings for signs of damage and corrosion. Check that all fixings are secure
  - o Check that cable entries are secure and water tight if applicable
  - o Check the termination box for signs of damage, corrosion or water ingress
  - o Open the environmental housing and check that there has been no water or dust ingress and ensure that there has been no infiltration of insects or vermin
  - o Inspect environmental housing seals and fastenings
  - o Check and verify enclosure heater is operational
  - o Verify and test all earth continuity bonding
  - o Test and document input power
  - o Clean the environmental housing window, inside and out
  - o Remove any unnecessary obstructions in the field of view
  - o Check focus and iris for optimum performance
  - o Check image quality and make any necessary electronic adjustments.

- Fully-Functional Cameras
  - o Carry out tests as above for a static camera
  - o Check all telemetry functions
  - o Check preset deployment
  - o Check wash-wipe functionality paying particular attention to the wiper blade

- o Check operation of illumination
- o Check operation of photo cell.

- Control Equipment
  - o Remove dust and waste from on top of and within enclosures
  - o Check ventilation is clear
  - o Check that forced ventilation fans are operational
  - o Clean or replace dust filters
  - o Check that all cables are supported and terminated correctly
  - o Clean all display screens as per manufacturer's instructions
  - o Check functionality of all buttons and indicators
  - o Measure and document all incoming signals
  - o Check full operation of all control equipment.

- Detection Systems
  - o Check operation of detection
  - o Check cause and effect integration.

- Digital Video Recording
  - o Check video retrieval
  - o Check time synchronisation
  - o Check duration of archive.

- Computers
  - o Check that correct services are running, up-to-date and that there are no unnecessary services running
  - o Check system log for errors
  - o Check that the system back-up and restore is operational
  - o Clean fans, filters and vents
  - o Check ventilation is operational
  - o Clean the hard disk by removing old and unnecessary files
  - o Defrag the hard disk.

- User Interface
  - Clean external surfaces
  - Check colour, contrast and brightness of display screens
  - Check keyboard, mouse and joystick operation
  - Verify all operational function.

EACS Check List

The following check lists are only provided for assistance and are not all-inclusive. Always refer to the manufacturer's literature for further guidance.

- General
  - Check that the system is in accordance with the specification
  - Check that all warning labels are in place
  - Check that all cables and containment are correctly supported
  - Check all equipment fixings are secure
  - Check that all glands and seals are in good condition.

- Doors

Although the doors and gates generally fall outside of the maintenance contract, each portal that has controlled or monitored access associated with it must be inspected. The door itself has to be reviewed to check for excessive damage or warping that could affect the operation of the system or the actual security of the door. The following non-security related items should be checked.

  - Door leaf/leaves
  - Hinges
  - Door closer
  - Door furniture
  - Door frame

- o   Any glazing associated with the door.

- Local Door Control Equipment
  - o   Check that all of the equipment is securely fixed
  - o   Check that the wiring connections are tight
  - o   Check the locks for operation and alignment
  - o   Test and document the lock input power
  - o   Check any cable loops for integrity
  - o   Test the tamper circuits
  - o   Check the door contacts/position switch for correct operation
  - o   Check the readers/identification devices for correct operation and reporting of transactions
  - o   Check the request to exit devices for operation
  - o   Check emergency egress equipment for correct, mechanical operation
  - o   All links to fire alarm (if applicable) should be checked
  - o   Clean all of the local equipment.

- Door Control Equipment
  - o   Check that the equipment is securely fixed
  - o   Check that the wiring connections are tight
  - o   Test and document the controller input power
  - o   Test and document the lock output power
  - o   Test and document the battery charging power
  - o   Check the date of and test the batteries
  - o   Check that the software configuration is correct
  - o   Check that the software back-up and restore is operational.

- Central Control Equipment
  - o   Check that the equipment is securely fixed
  - o   Check that the wiring connections are tight
  - o   Test and document the input power
  - o   Check that the correct software services are running, and up-to-date and that there are no unnecessary ones running

o   Check the system log for errors
o   Check that the system back-up and restore is operational
o   Clean the fans, filters and vents
o   Check that the ventilation is operational
o   Clean the hard disk by removing old and unnecessary files
o   Defrag the hard disk.

- User Interface.
  o   Clean the external surfaces
  o   Check the colour, contrast and brightness of display screens
  o   Check the keyboard and mouse operation
  o   Verify all operational functions
  o   Verify all alarm conditions.

IDS Check List

The following check lists are only provided for assistance and are not all-inclusive. Always refer to the manufacturer's literature for further guidance.

- General
  o   Check that the system is in accordance with the specification
  o   Check that all warning labels are in place
  o   Check that all cables and containment are correctly supported
  o   Check all equipment fixings are secure
  o   Check that all glands and seals are in good condition.

- Detectors
  o   Check and document input power
  o   Test detection field
  o   Check double knock if applicable

o Test tamper devices
o Ensure that there are no obstructions in the detection field
o Check for magnetic alignment if applicable
o Check for presence of insects
o Clean the device.

- Central Control Equipment.
    o Check that the equipment is securely fixed
    o Check that the wiring connections are tight
    o Test tamper devices
    o Check and document all circuit resistance values
    o Test and document the control equipment input power
    o Test and document the control equipment output power
    o Test and document the battery charging power
    o Check the date of and test the batteries
    o Replace batteries every three years
    o Check that the software configuration is correct
    o Check that the software back-up and restore is operational
    o Check the system log.

- Remote Keypad.
    o Clean the external surfaces
    o Check the colour, contrast and brightness of display screens
    o Check the keypad operation
    o Verify all operational functions
    o Test tamper devices.

- Warning Devices
    o Check that the equipment is securely fixed
    o Check that the wiring connections are tight
    o Check audible operation
    o Check visual operation
    o Test and document the battery charging power

- o Check the date of and test the batteries
- o Replace batteries every three years
- o Test tamper devices.

 Glossary

Glossary

4:3:	Standard TV aspect ratio. 4 units wide by 3 units high.
16:9:	Wide-screen aspect ratio. 16 units wide by 9 units high.
720i	Wide-screen resolution used to signify HDTV, made up from 1280 X 720 pixels. The 'i' indicates that the video is interlaced.
720p:	Wide-screen resolution used to signify HDTV, made up from 1280 X 720 pixels. The 'p' indicates that the video is progressive scanning.
802.11:	IEEE Standards covering the use of wireless networks.
1080i:	Wide-screen resolution used to signify HDTV, made up from 1920 X 1080 pixels. The 'i' indicates that the video is interlaced
1080p:	Wide-screen resolution used to signify HDTV, made up from 1920 X 1080 pixels. The 'p' indicates that the video is progressive scanning.
Aberration:	Anything that affects the reliability of an image.
AC:	Alternating Current. (Electrical).

209

Access Group:	A set of people or devices sharing the same attributes.
Access Level:	An access authority based upon a set of rules such as time zone and credentials.
Access Point:	The location of a controlled portal.
ACE:	Ancillary Control Equipment.
Activity Detection:	Detection of movement (activity) within the field of view of a camera.
Activity Report:	An event log maintained by a security management system of all monitored/detected activity within the security system.
Actuator:	A swing arm mechanism that pushes or pulls an automated gate.
AD:	Analogue to Digital.
Address:	A unique identifier for a device on a system.
AES:	Advanced Encryption Standard.
ADSL:	Asymmetric Digital Subscriber Line is a communications transmission medium that is generally TCP/IP data transmission with different upload and download speeds.
AES:	Automatic Electronic Shutter.
AGC:	Automatic Gain Control.
AI:	Auto Iris.
ALC:	Automatic Light (Level) Control. An electronic adjustment on a CCTV camera/lens

that allows compensation for bright areas within the field of view.

Alphanumeric: Text generation consisting of either or both letters and numbers.

Amplifier: An electronic circuit that increases a signal level.

Analogue: Continuously changing signal as opposed to digital.

AND: Logical function if two states are true then AND is true.

Angle of View: The angle between the two extremes at which light enters a CCTV camera.

Ancillary Device: Any device connected to a system that provides additional function or features beyond that of the basic system.

ANPR: Automatic Number Plate Recognition.

Annunciator: An audible or visual device that indicates an alarm or an unusual situation.

Anti-passback: An access control rule that stops a card or token being used and passed back to another to be used again.

Anti-tailgate: An access control device that stops more than one person entering an area when only one set of credentials has been read.

Aperture: The element of a lens that controls the amount of light that enters the lens array.

ARC:	Alarm Receiving Centre.
Archive:	Long-term storage location or device.
Armature:	In locking, the armature is the metal plate that is usually connected to the door and is attracted by an electromagnetic lock to hold the door fast.
Artifact:	Undesirable data caused and left behind by processing.
ASCII:	American Standard Code for Information Interchange. A set of 128 characters, each represented by a binary code.
Aspect Ratio:	The ratio between the width and height of an image.
Aspherical Lens:	A lens manufactured to allow more light through with less distortion.
Asynchronous:	A signal that is not synchronised with any other.
ATE:	Alarm Transmission Equipment.
ATS:	Alarm Transmission System.
Attenuation:	The reduction in size of a signal.
Audio Challenge:	Public address system linked to a CCTV system to communicate with people in the field of view of the camera.
Audit Trail:	Data that can reconstruct previous activity to establish criteria such as who, what, where, when etc.

Authentication:	Evidence/proof that the data has not been altered since first recording.
Auto Iris:	An automated mechanism that increases and decreases the amount of light travelling through a lens to match the requirements of the camera with the scene in order to produce a good quality image.
AVC:	Advanced Video Coding.
AWG:	American Wire Gauge – a standard wire diameter specification.
b:	Bit (binary data)
B:	Byte (binary data)
B-Frame:	Within MPEG video compression, the B-Frame is predicted from the nearest I and P Frames.
Back EMF:	A damaging voltage spike generated when an electromagnet is switched off.
Back Focus:	The distance between the rear of the lens and the image sensor.
Back Porch:	A flat section of a video signal at the trailing edge of a sync pulse.
Badge:	Term used in access control systems for a printed ID/access card.
Balanced Signal:	A signal that travels through two cores of a cable with a good rejection of induced interference.

Balun:	A device used to convert an unbalanced signal to a balanced one.
Bandwidth:	The range of frequencies that can be transmitted through any given medium.
Baud:	The rate at which data is transmitted.
BGU:	Break-Glass Unit.
Binary:	A code series of '1's and '0's that represents larger information at machine code level in a computer system.
Biometric:	The identification of people by measuring unique personal characteristics.
Bit:	Basic form of binary data, either a 1 or a 0.
Bitmap:	An image made up from individual pixels.
Bitrate:	The transmission speed of data measured in bits per second.
Black Level:	The part of a composite video signal that represents the colour (shade) black with a voltage level.
Blanking Level:	The start of a composite video signal that is the nominal voltage of the video waveform.
Bloom:	A defocusing of an area within a video scene.
BNC:	Bayonet-Neil-Concelman. A quick connect connector used for composite video cables.
Board Camera:	A miniature CCTV camera with exposed circuitry.

Bus:	A data path within a system.
Byte:	A digital 'word' made up from eight binary bits.
C Mount:	A standard CCTV lens screw mounting with the back plane located 17.5mm from the CCD chip.
CATV:	Community Antenna Television.
CCD:	Charge Coupled Device. The image sensor in a CCTV camera.
CCD Format:	The diagonal dimension of a CCD image sensor. In CCTV this is commonly 1', 2/3',1/2', 1/2.5', 1/2.7' 1/3', 1/4'.
CCTV:	Closed Circuit Television.
CD:	Compact Disk.
CD-RW:	Compact Disk – Read/Write. A CD that can be written to.
Chrominance:	The colour information contained within a video signal.
CIE:	Control and Indicating Equipment.
CIF:	Common Interchange Format. A digitised image made up from 352 X 288 pixels. Multiples of CIF are common. 2CIF = 704 X 288 pixels, 4CIF = 704 X 576 pixels. Etc.
Clone:	An exact duplicate.
CNI:	Critical National Infrastructure.

Coaxial Cable:	A common two-core cable for transmitting a CCTV composite video signal. The centre core is surrounded by a shielding braid which is the second conductive core providing protection from electromagnetic interference.
CODEC:	COmpressor/DECompressor. A system or device that encodes a signal for transmission.
Colour Bars:	A test pattern of vertical coloured bars used to test video transmission and display.
Colour Burst:	The part of a composite video signal that contains the reference information for the colour of the image.
Colour Temperature:	Describes the hue of the colour.
Composite Video:	A video signal that is made up from combined chrominance and luminance information.
Compression:	A system that reduces the data file size.
Contact:	A mechanical switch.
Contrast:	The difference between light and dark in a video image.
CPU:	Central Processing Unit.
Credential:	Anything that uniquely identifies an individual.
Crosstalk:	Interference that crosses from one circuit to another.
CRT:	Cathode Ray Tube. The glass screen element used in non-flat screen televisions and

monitors.

CS Mount:	A standard CCTV lens screw mounting with the back plane located 12.5mm from the CCD chip.
CSN:	Chip Serial Number.
DAT:	Digital Audio Tape.
Db:	Decibel, a unit used to express gain or loss.
DC:	Direct Current. (Electrical).
DD:	Direct Drive. A lens that is controlled by a reference voltage taken from the camera to adjust the iris to compensate for varying light levels.
Dead Test:	The testing of cables prior to connection.
Degauss:	The process of demagnetising. This is usually used to remove data from magnetic storage media such as cassette tape.
Depth of Field:	The term used to describe the area within a CCTV image that is in a usable focus.
Digital:	A two-position signal made up from high and low states as opposed to analogue.
DIP Switch:	Dual Inline Package. Micro-switches typically mounted on a circuit board.
Discrimination:	To distinguish between normal surroundings and unusual activity.
Disk Array:	An arrangement of hard disk drives used to

	provide increased or resilient storage of data.
Disk Drive:	Magnetic data storage device used in computer systems.
Door Forced:	An alarm generated by an access control system when a door is opened without authorisation from the system.
Door Held:	An alarm generated by an access control system when a door is not closed within an allowed timeframe after a legitimate opening.
Door Status:	In access control, door status is either open or closed.
Double Knock:	A technique that requires two activations of a device before an alarm event is raised.
DSP:	Digital Signal Processor. The section of electronics within a CCTV system that processes the captured video.
DST:	Daylight Saving Time. The one-hour time shift to extend the amount of daylight in the evening.
Dualtech:	The combination of two differing technologies to verify the same event.
Duplex:	A bi-directional communication system or any system that can perform two processes simultaneously.
DVI:	Digital Visual Interface.
DVD:	Digital Versatile Disk.

DVD-RW:	Digital Versatile Disk – Read/Write. A DVD that can be written to.
DVR:	Digital Video Recorder.
Dynamic Range:	The range between the smallest and largest amount that a system can process.
EACS:	Electronic Access Control System.
EI:	Electronic Iris.
ELV:	Extra Low Voltage.
EMCCD:	Electron Multiplying Charge Coupled Device.
EMF:	Electro-Motive Force.
Encryption:	The process of rearranging data so that it becomes unreadable without the correct encryption key.
Engineer Code:	A code number that when entered into a system allows engineering level parameters to be altered.
Environmental Housing:	In system terms, this means any protective enclosure.
EoL:	End of Line. Usually referring to the resistors in a monitored circuit.
EPROM:	Erasable Programmable Read-Only Memory. A memory chip used to store data within an electronic circuit.
Ethernet:	A local or wide area computer network.

Event:	Any incident that causes a system action.
Event Log:	A register of events.
Exact Copy:	A copy of an original recording where the data is exactly the same throughout.
Export:	Transfer of data from a primary device to a secondary location.
Fail-safe:	A lock that unlocks when the power is removed.
Fail-secure:	A lock that locks when the power is removed.
FAR:	False Acceptance Rate.
FAT:	Factory Acceptance Test.
Field:	One half of a TV frame which is made up from a series of scanned lines.
Field of View:	The maximum scene that can be viewed by a CCTV camera/lens combination.
FIPS:	The United States Federal Information Processing Standards.
Fixed Focus Lens:	A CCTV lens that is manufactured with a fixed focal length and therefore cannot be adjusted.
Flash Memory:	A storage device that can be electronically erased and reprogrammed.
FMR:	False Match Rate.
FO:	Fibre-Optic.

Focal Length:	The distance between the lens and the convergent focal point.
Focal Point:	The area within the optical path of a lens where light converges.
Focus Ring:	An adapter used to fit a C Mount lens to a CS Mount camera.
Frame:	In CCTV, a frame is a still section of a sequence of images that makes up the motion picture.
Frame Store:	An electronic circuit that captures, digitises and stores a CCTV frame.
Free Access:	A portal that does not need any authorisation to enter.
Free Exit:	An access controlled portal that does not need authorisation to leave the area.
Frequency:	The number of cycles of a signal per second.
Front Porch:	A flat section of a video signal at the leading edge of a sync pulse.
FRR:	False Rejection Rate.
F-Stop:	A term used to indicate the speed of a lens. The smaller the number, the more light can pass through the lens.
FTP:	Foil Twisted Pair (cable).
Fuzzy Logic	A decision making process based on multiple values that determines the probable result.

G:	Giga, a billion. The number suffixed by the 'G' has nine zeros after it if it were written in long hand. The 'G' is usually suffixed by a unit such as bytes. (GB)
Gain:	The increase or decrease of an electronic signal.
Genlock:	A process of synchronising a video signal with an external signal.
Gimbal	A bracket that can pivot in multiple directions.
GND:	An electronic abbreviation for GROUND.
GNI:	Guaranteed Non-Interruptible, usually in relation to power supply.
GPS Clock:	Time signal taken from a Global Positioning System.
Ground Loop:	Induced electrical currents introduced when a system has two or more ground potentials.
GSM:	Global System for Mobile Communications.
Guard Tour:	A system where a person must follow a predetermined route, logging onto an electronic system at set points and in the correct order.
GUI:	Graphical User Interface.
H.261/263/264:	H. Series video compression standards. These are common CCTV video standards developed by the Video Coding Experts Group in conjunction with the Moving Pictures Experts Group.

HAD:	Hole Accumulation Diode. A technology used in some CCD chips.
Hall Effect:	The induction of electricity through contact with a magnetic field.
Hard Disk:	A magnetic storage device for computer data.
Head End:	An electronic term for the equipment located at the extremes of a system such as the data gathering component or the user interface.
HD:	High Definition.
HDD:	Hard Disk Drive. Magnetic data storage device used in computer systems.
HDMI:	High Definition Multimedia Interface
HDTV:	High Definition Television. A term used to describe a system that produces video at a resolution of either 1280 X 720 pixels or 1920 X 1080 pixels.
Hertz (Hz):	Unit used to measure frequency, one cycle per second equals one Hertz.
HI:	Human Interface.
Horizontal Resolution:	The number of vertical pixels that make up the horizontal lines of a CCTV image.
Housing:	In system terms, this means any protective enclosure.
Hub:	A central component that connects multiple parts of a system.

Hum:	Term used to describe induced interference, usually at mains power frequency.
HV:	High Voltage. Typically above 1,500 volts DC or above 1,000 volts AC.
Hyper-HAD:	A variant of HAD technology.
Hz:	Abbreviation of Hertz.
IAS:	Intruder Alarm System.
ID:	Identification.
IDC:	Insulation Displacement Connector.
IDS:	Intruder Detection System.
IEEE:	Institute of Electrical and Electronic Engineers.
I-Frame:	Intra Frame. With MPEG video compression, the I-Frame is the reference frame.
I&HAS:	Intruder and Hold-up Alarm System.
Import:	Transfer of data from a secondary location device to a primary device.
I/O:	Input/Output.
Immunity:	The ability to resist electromagnetic interference.
Impedance:	The electronic property that restricts current flow.
Infrared Light:	A frequency of light that is not visible to the

human eye but can be seen by CCTV cameras.

IP: Index of Protection. The rating system that uses a pair of numbers to describe the enclosure's protection against environmental conditions such as dust and water.

IP: Internet Protocol. The communication technology used on computer networks.

IR: Infrared (light).

IR Cut: A lens that has been machined to compensate for the refractive angle of infrared light.

Iris: A circular mechanical shutter that alters the amount of light that travels through a lens to match the requirements of the camera with the scene to produce a good quality image.

iSCSI: Internet Small Computer System Interface.

ISO: International Organisation for Standards.

IT: Information Technology.

JPEG: Joint Photographic Experts Group. The group that recommended and gave its name to a compression algorithm used for still digital images.

K: Kilo, a thousand. The number suffixed by the 'K' has three zeros after it if it were written in long hand. The 'K' is usually suffixed by a unit such as bytes. (KB)

Keep: A door lock mounted within a door frame – see 'Strike'.

LAN:	Local Area Network. A computer network that is confined to a certain area such as within a building.
Latching:	A switch that stays 'switched' when pressed. Usually un-latches when pressed again.
LCD:	Liquid Crystal Display.
LED:	Light Emitting Diode.
Lens:	The optical device that focuses light onto the image sensor of a CCTV camera.
Lens Speed:	Refers to the aperture of a lens. A large aperture allows more light in which in turn allows a faster shutter speed.
Level:	Generally used to refer to the amount of power in a signal.
Line-Locked:	The synchronisation of a video signal with the frequency of the AC power.
Lockdown:	A one-operation command to secure a building or facility.
Lock Status:	In access control, lock status is either locked, unlocked or tamper.
Luminance:	The level within a video signal that dictates the brightness of the image.
Lux:	The unit used to measure the illumination of a surface.
LV:	Low Voltage. Typically between 120 and 1,500 volts DC or between 50 and 1,000 volts

AC.

m:	Milli, a thousandth. The number suffixed by the 'm' is shifted to the right by three decimal places if it were written in long hand. The 'm' is usually suffixed by a unit such as metres (mm).
M:	Mega, a million. The number suffixed by the 'M' has six zeros after it if it were written in long hand. The 'M' is usually suffixed by a unit such as bytes (MB).
Maglock:	Electromagnetic lock.
Manual Iris:	A manual mechanism that increases and decreases the amount of light travelling through a lens to match the requirements of the camera with the scene to produce a good quality image.
Manual Zoom:	A lens that can be adjusted across a focal length range and the lens array adjusts proportionally to maintain focus.
Master Copy:	An exact copy of data made from an original recording.
Matrix:	In CCTV, a matrix is a video-switching device that will present any number of cameras to any number of monitors.
Microwave:	A very high frequency electromagnetic wave used in transmission and detection systems.
Metadata:	Small amounts of data that record details of larger amounts of data.

Monitor:	Display screen.
Monochrome:	Video or any image made up only from the greyscale.
MPEG:	Motion Picture Experts Group. The group that recommended and has given its name to several compression algorithms used for moving digital images.
Multi-mode Fibre:	Fibre-optic cable that has a larger core which simplifies connection. Multi-mode fibre has a higher attenuation on the signal carried within it compared to a single-mode cable.
Multiplex:	To interleave multiple video streams.
MW:	Microwave.
n:	Nano, a billionth. The number suffixed by the 'n' is shifted to the right by nine decimal places if it were written in long hand. The 'n' is usually suffixed by a unit such as metres (nm).
NAND:	Logical function if one or two states are untrue then NAND is true.
Network Switch:	A computer network device that links other devices together.
NIC:	Network Interface Card. The component part of a device that connects it to a computer network.
NFC:	Near Field Communications.
NO/NC:	Normally Open/Normally Closed. Indicating

the rest state of a switch.

Noise:	Interference induced into a signal.
Non-Latching:	A switch that only operates momentarily when pressed.
NOR:	Logical function if two states are untrue then NOR is true.
NTP:	Network Time Protocol.
NTSC:	National Television System Committee. The group that gave its name to and set the standard for analogue colour television used in the United States. The standard is used in several other countries. NTSC has 525 TV Lines per frame and 30 frames per second.
NVR:	Network Video Recorder. A CCTV recording device that sits on a local or wide area network.
OCR:	Optical Character Recognition.
Ohm:	The unit of electrical resistance.
O/P:	Output.
Operator Code:	A code number that when entered into a system allows an operator or user to access only the information and settings available to them.
OR:	Operational Requirements.
OR:	Logical function if one or two states are true then OR is true.

Original Recording:	The first instance of recorded data.
Overscan:	The part of a video signal that is not displayed on a CRT screen because the raster extends beyond the display area.
Overvoltage Suppression:	A device that protects electronic circuits from high-voltage spikes.
P:	Peta, a million billion. The number suffixed by the 'P' has 15 zeros after it if it were written in long hand. The 'P' is usually suffixed by a unit such as bytes. (PB)
PA:	Public Address
PA:	Personal or Panic Alarm.
PAL:	Phase Alternating Line. A European analogue colour television standard. PAL has 625 TV Lines per frame and 25 frames per second.
Passback:	In access control, the activity of a person using a credential to gain entry to an area and then passing that credential back to another to enable them to enter as well.
PC:	Personal Computer, usually referring to a desktop computer.
PCB:	Printed Circuit Board.
Peak to Peak:	The voltage difference between the top and bottom points of an electronic waveform.
P-Frame:	Predicted Frame. With MPEG video compression, the P-Frame is predicted from

the I-Frame.

PIA:	Privacy Impact Assessment
PIDS:	Perimeter Intrusion Detection System.
PIN:	Personal Identification Number.
Pinhole Lens:	A CCTV lens designed to see through a very small aperture, often used in covert situations.
PIR:	Passive Infrared (detector).
PIV:	Personal Identity Verification.
Pixel:	A single element of an imaging device or resultant image.
Phased Locked Loop (PLL):	An oscillating electronic circuit that locks on to the phase of an input signal.
Point ID:	The ability to identify the location of the event.
Polling:	A system sends a regular signal to a remote device and the remote device answers the signal to prove communications are operating.
Portal:	In access control, an opening that will allow a person or vehicle to enter an area.
Pot:	Potentiometer. In CCTV, used to determine the position of a PT motor.
Port:	A communications connection.
PPM:	Planned or Periodic Preventative Maintenance
Pre-Amp:	Electronic circuit that increases a signal prior

to transmission or processing.

Pre-Set Position: In CCTV, a term used to describe a pre-programmed position that a PT motor will return to when instructed.

Profile: In access control, a profile is a database entry that identifies an individual and details where they can go and when.

PROM: Programmable Read-Only Memory. A memory chip used to store data within an electronic circuit.

Protocol: The format or language of data between systems.

Prox: When used in relation to access control, 'prox' is short for proximity which is the ability to read card data without having to connect the card with the reader.

PSIM: Physical Security Information Management system

PSU: Power Supply Unit.

PT: Pan and Tilt. The mechanism that positions a CCTV camera.

PTE: Push to Exit. A button used to request a legitimate exit from the secure side of an access-controlled door.

PTZ: Pan, Tilt and Zoom. The combined motor and lens mechanisms that position a CCTV camera.

Pulse:	Either part of a signal or a momentary change in current or voltage.
QCIF:	Quarter CIF (Resolution).
REX:	Request to Exit. A signal used to request a legitimate exit from the secure side of an access-controlled door.
RF:	Radio Frequency.
RFID:	Radio Frequency Identification.
RAID:	Redundant Array of Independent Disks.
RAM:	Random Access Memory.
Raster:	The scan lines that make up an analogue television image.
Reflectance:	The level at which light reflects from a surface.
Resolution:	The amount of detail contained within a CCTV image, either made up from TV Lines (TVL) or the number of Pixels.
RGB:	Red, Green, Blue. The colour components of a television signal.
RJ45:	Standard connector for computer networks.
ROM:	Read-Only Memory.
Router:	A computer network device that sends data.
RS-232/422/485:	A serial data format.
RX:	Receive.

SAB:	Self-Actuating Bell. A term still used to describe external audible warning devices on an intruder detection system.
Salvo	A series of switched events, typically an array of video images switched to multiple monitors.
SAN:	Storage Area Network.
SAT:	Site Acceptance Test.
Saturation:	The intensity of the colours within a video signal.
SC:	Subscriber Connector. An optical fibre connector.
SCSI:	Small Computer System Interface.
SD:	Standard Definition.
SDSL:	Symmetric Digital Subscriber Line. Communications transmission medium, generally TCP/IP data transmission with the same upload and download speeds.
Serial Data:	Transmission of data, one bit at a time.
Serial Interface:	The link between two devices that allows the transmission of serial data.
Serial Port:	The port on a computer that allows external communications, usually via RS-232.
Shunt:	Deliberately isolating a circuit by introducing a short circuit.
Shutter Speed:	In CCTV, this is the period of time taken for a

single image to be captured.

Signal to Noise Ratio (S/N):	The ratio of noise to actual signal.
Simplex:	A communication system that works in one direction only or any system that can only do one thing at a time.
Single-Mode Fibre:	A fibre-optic cable with a small diameter core. A single-mode fibre offers less attenuation to the signal carried within it.
SMS:	Short Messaging Service. Text message via the mobile phone network.
SMS:	Security Management System.
Soak:	A test period where a system is left operational to see if there will be any natural failures.
SOP:	Standard Operating Procedure. A procedure documented to prompt the reader on how to deal with any given event.
ST:	Straight Tip. An optical fibre connector.
STP:	Shielded Twisted Pair (cable).
Strike:	In reference to an electric lock, a strike is the movable front plate that when locked will not let a latch from a door lock pass. Also known as a keep.
SVGA:	Super Video Graphic Array
S-VHS:	Super VHS video tape format.

Synchronised:	A signal that is aligned with another.
T:	Tera, a thousand billion. The number suffixed by the 'T' has 12 zeros after it if it were written in long hand. The 'T' is usually suffixed by a unit such as bytes. (TB)
Tailgate:	In access control, the act of following an authorised person through a controlled portal.
Tamper Switch:	A switch fitted to a piece of equipment that will activate if the cover is removed or screws loosened.
TCP/IP:	Data language – Transmission Control Protocol/Internet Protocol.
TDG:	Time Date Generator.
Telemetry:	Remote control via an electronic signal.
Text Generator:	A system element that inserts alpha-numeric text into a video signal such as a camera number or the time and date.
TFT:	Thin Film Transistor.
Threshold:	The level of any measurement above which an alarm is generated.
Time-lapse:	In CCTV, a method of recording by sampling an image every set period of time. e.g. one mage per second. When played back at normal speed (25 or 30 images per second) the recoding appears to be speeded up. This process allows long periods of time to be stored on relatively small media.

Transaction:	Any access control event associated with the unlocking of a portal.
Transient:	A brief surge of electricity in a circuit.
Transient Suppression:	A device that protects electronic circuits from high voltage spikes.
TTL:	Transistor Transistor Logic.
TV:	Television.
TV Lines (TVL):	The horizontal scans that make up an analogue television image.
Twisted Pair:	A cable made up from multiples of two cores. Each pair of cores is twisted together to reduce induced noise.
TX:	Transmit.
UAV:	Unmanned Aerial Vehicle.
UHF:	Ultra-High Frequency.
UI:	User Interface
Unbalanced Signal:	In CCTV, an electronic signal that travels through the centre core only of a coaxial cable.
Underscan:	In CCTV, reduces the scan size so that the entire image can be seen on a monitor.
UPS:	Uninterruptible Power Supply.
User Code:	A code number that when entered into a system allows an operator or user to access only the information and settings available to

them.

UTP:	Unshielded Twisted Pair (cable).
VCA:	Video Content Analysis.
VDA:	Video Distribution Amplifier.
Verification:	Any technique used to reduce nuisance within an automated detection system.
Varifocal:	A lens that can be adjusted across a focal length range but where the lens array does not adjust proportionally to maintain focus.
Vertical Resolution:	The number of horizontal pixels that make up the vertical columns of a CCTV image.
VGA:	Video Graphics Array.
VHF:	Very High Frequency.
VHS:	Video Home System.
VMD:	Video Motion Detection.
WAN:	Wide Area Network. A computer network that extends beyond the local area such as within a building. The WAN would connect buildings separated by considerable distances.
WASS:	Wide Area Surveillance System.
Wavelet:	A type of video compression.
WD:	Warning Device. Any device that alerts an operator to an event.

WDR:	Wide Dynamic Range. In CCTV, the ability to process a wide range of different light levels simultaneously.
Wiegand:	A protocol for sending data used in access control systems.
White Balance:	In CCTV, an adjustment to retain true colours.
White Level:	The part of a composite video signal that represents the colour (shade) white with a voltage level.
White Noise:	Multi-frequency interference.
Working Copy:	Duplicate data recorded for further processing.
WORM:	Write Once Read Many. A media form that can only be written to on one occasion, After that it can only be read.
Y/C:	A video format made up from separate Luminance (Y) and Chrominance (C) signals.
Z & L:	Mounting brackets that allow a maglock to be installed above a door and the armature plate to be lifted to meet the magnet. These brackets are used for inward opening doors.
Zoom Lens:	A lens with the ability to change its focal length either manually or with a motor.
Zoom Ratio:	The ratio between a lens's maximum and minimum focal lengths.

 Illustrations

Table of Illustrations

Table of Illustrations

Table of Illustrations

Index

Index